PRE-COLUMBIAN
ART

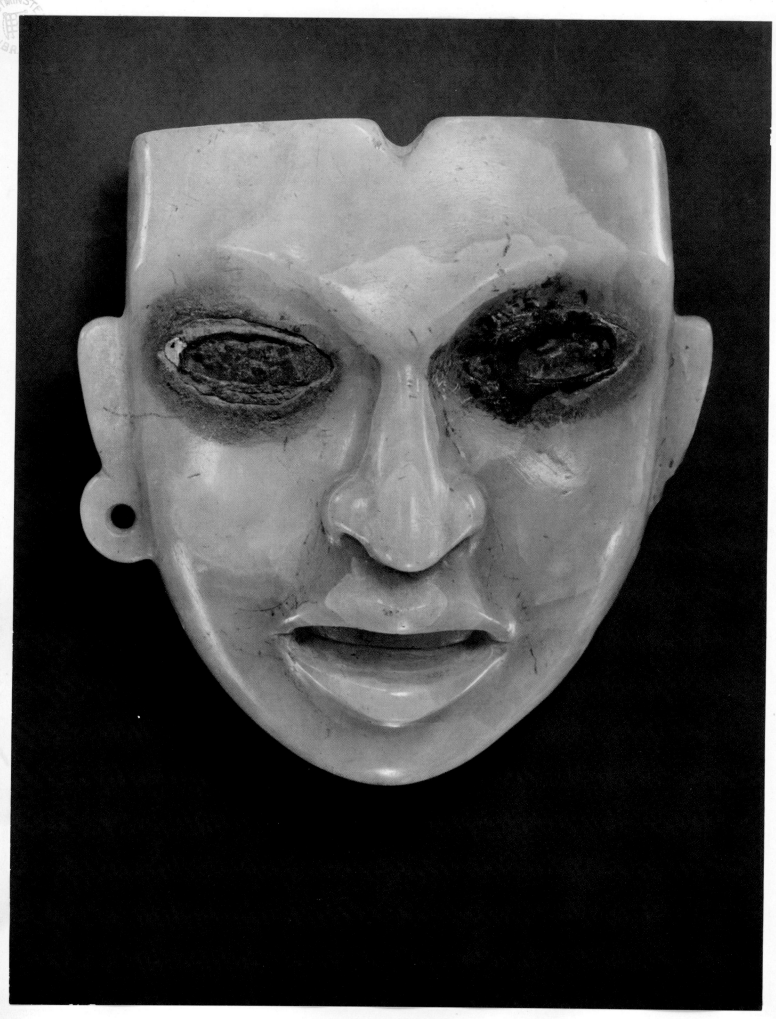

Onyx marble mask. Style of Teotihuacan. Mexico. *Cat. No. 35.*

ROBERT WOODS BLISS
COLLECTION

PRE-COLUMBIAN ART

TEXT AND CRITICAL ANALYSES BY

S·K·LOTHROP

W·F·FOSHAG

JOY MAHLER

WITH 270 ILLUSTRATIONS

PUBLISHED BY THE PHAIDON PRESS
LONDON · MCMLVII

COLOUR BLOCKS ENGRAVED BY SCHWITTER AG · BASLE

COLOUR PLATES PRINTED BY V · S · K · PRINTERS · BASLE

TEXT SET AND PRINTED BY HUNT · BARNARD & CO LTD

AT THE SIGN OF THE DOLPHIN · AYLESBURY · BUCKS

BOUND BY A · W · BAIN & CO LTD · LONDON

CONTENTS

PREFACE

SOON after reaching Paris in the spring of 1912, my friend Royall Tyler took me to a small shop in the Boulevard Raspail to see a group of pre-Columbian objects from Peru. I had just come from the Argentine Republic, where I had never seen anything like these objects, the temptations offered there having been in the form of colonial silver. Within a year, the *antiquaire* of the Boulevard Raspail, Joseph Brummer, showed me an Olmec jadeite figure (No. 8 of the Catalogue). That day the collector's microbe took root in - it must be confessed - very fertile soil. Thus, in 1912, were sown the seeds of an incurable malady!

These first objects are the base upon which I have slowly built my collection. From these, and the reading of archaeological books on Mexico, Central and South America, came the conviction that the sculpture, the goldsmiths' work, textiles and ceramics of the inhabitants of the Western Hemisphere before the voyages of Columbus were often of great artistic value; and that they belong in Museums of Art as well as in the crowded cases of archaeological artifacts or folk-art in museums of natural history. As time went on, I would now and again acquire in Europe or in the United States examples of fine workmanship or of an arresting concept. But not one did I ever find in the country of its origin! So, in publishing their likenesses it might be said that, in a way, I am returning them to the countries in which they were created.

In a nomadic career spreading over years of close contact with the grindstone of diplomatic life, there were many periods when no temptation came to my door. But always, in lean years or in full, the encouraging enthusiasm and the discrimination of my wife have helped to make this collection what it is.

Although somewhat skeptical of the results, my friends Dr. David E. Finley, Director of the National Gallery of Art, and Mr. John Walker, Chief Curator, suggested that it might be an interesting experiment to exhibit my material and see if it found favor with the public. The collection has remained at the Gallery on loan since 1947 and the steadily increasing response of a large and interested public seems to have justified their kind decision. For the continuing generosity of time and space and for the hospitality given to this collection of indigenous art, I am most grateful to the Director and the Chief Curator.

The publication of this catalogue is due, largely, to the insistence of friends that the collection be made known to those interested in pre-Columbian art who may be unable to visit Washington and, more especially, to the people inhabiting the countries in which the objects originated. It is presented in the hope that it will increase the knowledge of these early cultures, and the enjoyment that a greater familiarity with them may bring.

Washington, May 21, 1956.   R. W. B.

ACKNOWLEDGMENTS

AMONG the many to whom I am beholden in the preparation of this book, my greatest debt is to Dr. Samuel K. Lothrop. I hope he will realize how lasting is my obligation to him. As was the case in preparing the handbook of the collection in 1947 ("Indigenous Art of the Americas"), the continued association with his well-stored mind has been as enjoyable as it has been enriching. Dr. Lothrop has devoted his time and vast knowledge to planning the catalogue and to writing the text. In designing the plates he was ably assisted by Mr. Nickolas Muray, to whom I am indebted for the excellence of his work in photographing the objects and I offer especial thanks to Miss Joy Mahler of the Peabody Museum of Harvard University for her meticulous care in preparing the description of the textiles.

Dr. Lothrop wishes to associate himself with me in expressing deep appreciation to that distinguished anthropologist and administrator, Dr. Paul Fejos, President and Director of Research of the Wenner-Gren Foundation, who has been most generous of his time in giving sound advice on the selection of the format, as well as on problems of publication. For his friendly counsel we are indeed grateful.

For additional helpful suggestions kindly given by Miss Cordelia Galt, former Peabody Museum editor, Dr. Lothrop and I offer her our sincere thanks.

The unexpected loss suffered by the Smithsonian Institution in the sudden death this morning of the world-renowned mineralogist, Dr. William F. Foshag, has shocked both Dr. Lothrop and me. As Head Curator of the Department of Geology of the United States National Museum, Dr. Foshag generously shared his erudition with us. Despite crowded hours, he always made time to identify the geological substances of any hard stone objects which I submitted to him, which, together with his treatise, greatly add to the authority of this book.

The maps are reproduced through the courtesy of the National Geographic Society and The Museum of Modern Art in New York. For this important contribution in completing the catalogue, we express our warm thanks to Mr. Francis W. Sheppard of The National Geographic Magazine and to Mr. René d'Harnoncourt, Director of the Museum.

For identification and authentication of individual objects in the collection we are particularly grateful to the following persons: Junius B. Bird and Dr. Gordon F. Ekholm of The American Museum of Natural History; to Dr. Matthew B. Stirling, Director of the Bureau of American Ethnology of the Smithsonian Institution; to Dr. A. V. Kidder, Miss Tatiana Proskouriakoff and J. Eric S. Thompson of the Carnegie Institution of Washington; to Miss Isabelle Guernsey, F. P. Orchard and the late Dr. Alfred Tozzer of the Peabody Museum at Harvard. Assistance in establishing the provenance of numerous pieces has been given by Charles A. Balser, Karl P. Curtis, Charles Ratton, Earl Stendahl and John Wise, to whom I extend my thanks.

The late Charles M. Richards, former Registrar of the National Gallery of Art, was unfailingly helpful, as was the Assistant Registrar, Miss Katharine Shepard. It distresses me that this expression of special appreciation could not have reached Mr. Richards before his so regrettable and sudden death. I also extend my thanks to William P. Campbell, the present Registrar of the Gallery, as well as to Miss Elizabeth Polk Benson, Assistant Registrar.

Lastly, but far from least, it is to Dr. Perry B. Cott, Assistant Curator of the National Gallery, that I owe special thanks for the subtle and distinguished arrangement of the collection. Despite his heavy duties, the time and ingenuity he has given to enlarging the exhibition space and to placing the objects, often so dissimilar in material, style, size and mood, has given me a most delightful experience. During the past year he has been ably seconded by Dr. H. Lester Cooke to whom, as well as to the other members of the Gallery staff, and to the Guards, I offer my sincere thanks for the many courtesies they have extended to me.

Washington, May 21, 1956.   R. W. B.

INTRODUCTION

THE OBJECTS illustrated and described in this volume represent the finest craftsmanship and skill of aboriginal America. Few of these artifacts can be regarded as folk art; the bulk of the collection consists of objects manufactured for the aristocrats of their day who deemed them to be of high artistic merit. Furthermore, they represent a wide range in time and space, and they reflect many and varied stylistic traditions.

The relative skills and merits of New World artifacts cannot be assessed entirely by our own standards. Montezuma, the Aztec emperor, told Cortés that jades were his most precious possession and that he valued both turquoise and long green plumes of the quetzal bird even more than gold. This appraisal of jade extended far into the past. A Maya jade inscribed with a date is known to have been cherished above ground for fully a thousand years before it was interred with its then owner.

Europeans, until recently, have been apathetic to native American art, notably so in the nations most active in establishing colonial empires. The first great treasure to reach Europe was part of the loot of Mexico sent to Spain by Cortés. The Royal Historian published a detailed description and stated: 'I do not marvel at gold and precious stones. But am in a manner astonished to see the workmanship excel the substance.' The Spaniards, however, melted the gold and silver; for the most part they lost or discarded the textiles, feather-work, wood carvings and jades. What little survives today consists of a few Mexican objects sent as curiosities to friends, mostly in Austria and Italy. No authenticated artifact from the loot of Central or South America is on record in Spain or elsewhere.

Two of three treasure ships dispatched by Cortés were captured by the French pirate Jean Florin. Nothing, however, is known of what happened to their cargoes except that Montezuma's great pyramidal emerald was recut and became part of the French crown jewels. It was lost at the time of the French revolution. Little survives from the early French contacts with North American Indians.

The British attitude towards aboriginal American artifacts also has been marked by indifference until recently. Yet the first purchasers of Cortés' loot were individual Englishmen of wealth who made the so-called Grand Tour of Europe towards the end of the eighteenth century, resulting in the great collection now in the British Museum. Furthermore, in 1920, the Burlington Fine Arts Club held in London one of the first exhibitions which displayed New World products as art rather than curiosities.

In the United States, interest in aboriginal art has been aroused largely through individual collectors of archaeological material. Apart from such excavated artifacts, however, few objects more than a century old are preserved. Many United States museums devoted to art, however, possess aboriginal collections, and some keep them on permanent view. Increasing public interest has resulted in various large-scale loan exhibits of outstanding specimens. At the same time, university museums, whose primary function is background for teaching, are revising their installations to display to better advantage the beauty of individual objects.

The Bliss collection covers the range of higher New World cultures from Mexico to Peru. It contains no objects from the sixteenth-century loot, for only two have appeared for sale in Europe during the present century. Although the collection is then entirely archaeological, there are delicate materials which normally disappear in the ground, such as cotton, wool, feathers and wood, preserved owing to unusual climatic conditions. There also are artifacts which have been prized by previous owners and may have a known history over the past century.

A general discussion of aboriginal America is not possible or desirable in this Introduction. We shall outline briefly, however, what is now known about the cultures represented in the Bliss collection and estimate so far as is possible the period when they flourished. In each area we shall start with the oldest known art forms.

S. K. L.

CULTURES AND STYLES

by S. K. Lothrop

CULTURES AND STYLES

CENTRAL AND EASTERN MEXICO

THIS term covers Mexico City, the Valley of Mexico and parts of adjacent states to the east, an area which has been one of the most intensively studied in the New World. Hence there is correspondingly great knowledge concerning its past. The first inhabitants, many thousand years ago, were nomadic primitive hunters who slaughtered animals now extinct.

Archaic or Formative culture. Radiocarbon tests indicate that before 1500 B.C. what is today known as the Archaic culture had come into existence. We know nothing about the linguistic or ethnic background of its creators but they were far from primitive, for they lived in settled communities, practised agriculture, manufactured pottery including figurines of great originality (Pl. i, *top left*), and had mastered the art of jade carving. They contributed little, however, to the styles and symbolism of later eras.

Olmec (La Venta) culture. Olmec is a term primarily applied to the sixteenth-century inhabitants of the southern part of the State of Vera Cruz, concerning whom little is known. It is also used to denote an art style dating from a very much earlier period, which was only detected about 30 years ago in the same region. La Venta is the name of one of the principal archaeological sites but is a term better suited to describe a special phase rather than the whole culture. Olmec art is known to have been contemporary in part with the Archaic culture in the Mexican highlands, and it flourished until the end of the Classical Maya period. Its influence was felt over a wide area, and stray trade pieces even reached Costa Rica and Panama.

Olmec remains include civic centers with large ceremonial courts surrounded by mounds of earth. In them are found megalithic carvings including stelae, altars and colossal heads measuring up to twenty feet in circumference (fig. 1), pottery of diversified types, and some of the finest jade carvings known in the New World (Pls. i-x).

Olmec carving is especially pleasing to the eye trained in European art because of relatively simple symbolism and broad treatment, especially in portraying the

15

Fig. 1. *Monumental Olmec carving*. Height, 8 ft. 1 in. Circumference 20 ft. 10 in. Courtesy National Geographic Society.

human body. Carvings, whether in relief or in the round, have a realism and dynamic quality rarely found in neighbouring art strains such as the Maya. Symbolism is largely confined to representation of a Jaguar god; hence the flamboyant serpent and plumed serpent motif of adjacent or later cultures are absent.

The Olmec possessed their own writing system and they recorded dates perhaps in the same manner as the Maya. If the Olmec calendar had the same starting point as the Maya, the most ancient dates in the New World must be attributed to them. In fact, they may have invented a calendar which the Maya took over and elaborated.

Teotihuacan culture. The ancient city of Teotihuacan in the Valley of Mexico, famous for its great pyramids of the Sun and the Moon, has given its name to art styles which have been traced to Guatemala, Honduras and El Salvador. At present, four successive phases are recognized, which in time extend from Late Archaic in Central Mexico to the culmination and decline of Classic Maya. The culture is so complex that further subdivisions must be anticipated in the future.

Teotihuacan represents one of the great existing architectural achievements of ancient Mexico (figs. 2, 3). An unusual feature is that many of the frescoes which adorned its walls have been preserved (Pl. xxv). Furthermore, the fresco technique was transferred to pottery vessels, the walls of which might be coated with plaster and painted with complex designs (Pls. xxxi-xxxiv). A new symbolism appeared, based primarily on new gods, birds and snakes, as well as 'filler patterns' to eliminate blank spaces. These became traditions which persisted with varying intensity in later cultures until the Spanish conquest.

Teotihuacan produced large stone sculptures, often of barbaric complexity. At the same time, there existed a simpler style in stone sculpture, exemplified in figurines (Pl. xxx) and so-called masks, which are approximately life-size human faces carved in stone (Pls. xxvii, xxviii and frontispiece). These are not encumbered by complex religious symbolism and perhaps may represent a survival of Olmec tradition although the styles are distinct. What purpose these masks served is not known.

Classic Veracruz (Tajín or Totonac) culture. In central Vera Cruz, there is a confusion of names similar to that in the southern part of the State. Totonac, like the word Olmec, is primarily an ethnic term applied to the sixteenth-century inhabitants. It has also been attached to an art strain dating many centuries earlier, partly contemporaneous with Classic Maya. In recent years the name of the principal ancient city, Tajín, has been substituted for Totonac, but this term applies best to a special phase.

Classic Veracruz art embraces architectural remains of importance (fig. 4) as well as stelae and bas-reliefs and a number of smaller stone carvings of curious forms. The style tends towards realism overlaid with abstractions such as multiple

Fig. 3. *Teotihuacan from the air*. The Temple of the Sun, still over 200 ft. high, is in the center.
Courtesy American Museum of Natural History.

scroll motifs. It thus is closer to Teotihuacan or Classic Maya than to Olmec. All three must have had a partial overlap in time.

Classic Veracruz art is best known through several kinds of curiously shaped carvings which have been the subject of much speculation. One group, called stone yokes, consists of U-shape stones about the size of an ox yoke, often covered with elaborate adornment (Pls. xii and xiii). These objects have been

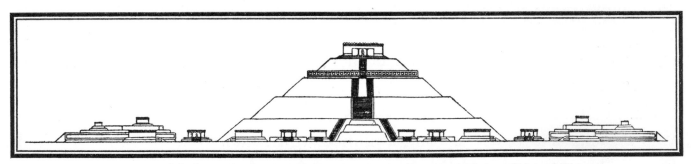

Fig. 2. *Restored sky line at Teotihuacan*. After Gamio. Courtesy American Museum of Natural History.

Fig. 4. *Model of a Classic Veracruz pyramid at El Tajín, Mexico.* Courtesy American Museum of Natural History.

identified with body protectors worn by players in ball games, played in masonry courts, as shown on reliefs and figurines. The ball was of solid rubber and heavy and, as the players were not allowed to touch it with their hands, severe injuries might be inflicted and some protection was necessary. Whether the stone yokes were purely ceremonial or were actually used is open to argument. Perhaps a lighter substitute was employed in play; on the other hand, striking power may have been substituted for speed of foot. At any rate, the stone yokes actually fit the human waist snugly, and cause surprisingly little inconvenience in spite of their weight.

A second type of Classic Veracruz artifact is known as a *palma* or palmate stone (Pl. xxiii). It has a massive curved base surmounted by an arched panel. This forms the background for a figure in relief, human or animal usually, which may be embellished with scroll patterns. These are of a different type from those normally associated with the stone yokes, probably indicating a difference in date.

Palmas have been identified as ornaments worn with the curved base resting on a large belt.

Another group of carvings, known as *hachas* or ceremonial axes, are thin plaques with a notch at the base and a curved blade running across the top and down one side (Pls. xvi and xvii). Each of the flat sides normally is carved in relief and often represents a human head in profile, but the stone normally is too narrow to carve in the round. *Hachas,* which are smaller and much lighter than *palmas,* also were worn above thick belts.

Intermediate between *palmas* and *hachas* there is another Classic Veracruz type which conforms more or less to the *hacha* in outline but is thick enough to represent a head in the round. In this small group, however, the head usually represents a trophy with closed eyes, gaping mouth and hair shaved to form a crest (Pls. xx-xxii). This in turn suggests that human sacrifice was performed in conjunction with the ceremonial ball games.

These four types of carvings, especially the yokes and *hachas,* evidently were esteemed by the Maya of the Classic period, for examples have been found in their cities as far south as Honduras and El Salvador. The distribution in Middle America is then the same as the masonry ball-court.

Tula-Toltec culture. The first group in Mexico to emerge with a vague recorded history was the Toltec, a Nahua-speaking people, who settled at Tula in the State of Hidalgo about A.D. 900. There has been much confusion concerning the Toltec because literary sources, recorded after the Conquest, are not in agreement. Until recently, it was thought that the Toltec were the builders of Teotihuacan and the creators of its culture. It is now generally agreed that they built the city of Tula and also the part of Chichen Itza in Yucatan which is almost identical in style. Both archaeological and historical data indicate that the Tula-Toltec regime broke up as a result of crop failures in the middle of the twelfth century. Many migrated to Central America. At the time of the Conquest, individuals still boasted of their Toltec ancestry.

The Toltec were regarded by other Mexicans as innovators of culture, and a ruler named Quetzalcoatl or Kukulcan, the Feathered Serpent, was the cultural hero. It is true that about the tenth century A.D. new architectural (fig. 5) and ceramic forms appeared and the use of metals in Mexico began. A notable social development was the creation of warrior societies, the Knights of the Eagle and

Fig. 5. *Reconstruction of Toltec architectural style at Chichen Itza, Yucatan.*
Courtesy Carnegie Institution of Washington.

Knights of the Jaguar. These persisted until Aztec times and their symbols became important in art. The Aztec pantheon had its beginnings both in Teotihuacan and southern Mexico, but the Toltec also contributed greatly to it, and supposedly they introduced or popularized the rite of human sacrifice which was to become so important later.

Tarascan culture. The country west of the central Mexican plateau was occupied in the sixteenth century by several groups speaking different tongues, of which the most important were the Tarascans who defeated the Aztec in battle. Their capital was Tzintzuntzan, the Place of the Humming Birds. This area was noted for its feather mosaics, unfortunately a fugitive art medium. Archaeology has revealed a highly developed folk art in pottery, distinguished by vigor, humor and freedom from religious symbolism. Effigy vessels are typical (Pl. lxi, *bottom*). They represent men, women, children and dogs, often with considerable attempt at realism.

Aztec culture. The Aztec were the principal military power crushed by the Spaniards and, as such, they received more literary notice than their neighbors. As a military power, they held large areas in tribute which resulted in a great

Fig. 6. *Aztec pyramid and temples at Tenayuca, Mexico.* Top: model showing restoration. Bottom: the stairway.
Courtesy American Museum of Natural History.

concentration of wealth. Furthermore, they traded with areas they did not control as far south as Panama.

The Aztec were late-comers in the Valley of Mexico, migrants from the north. Their period of power lasted less than two centuries. Much of their culture was adopted from their neighbors. Nevertheless, they developed artists skilled in stone carving (Pls. xxxv-xlviii), metalwork (Pl. l) and featherwork, as well as in the construction of huge temples (fig. 6).

Aztec art is massive and somber. Like their religion, dominated by human sacrifice, it deals with pain and death. Skulls (Pls. xlvi-xlviii), barbaric serpents (Pls. xl-xlii), priests clad in the flayed skins of the sacrificed (Pl. xlv) are typical subjects of sculpture. On the other hand, their lapidaries and metalworkers produced some of the finest and most delicate jewelry of aboriginal America (Pl. l).

Vessels made from onyx marble (frequently referred to as alabaster) are nowhere common but they are found from Central Mexico to Costa Rica, including the Maya area and Honduras (q.v.). The chief source of onyx marble in Mexico was the town of Tecali - the Aztec name for this material - in the State of Puebla. One of the great manufacturing centers was the Isla de Sacrificios off Vera Cruz. Another existed in the State of Oaxaca where a stone with a green tinge was mined.

The use of onyx marble for vessels in Mexico seems to date from the end of the Teotihuacan period but most examples probably are contemporary with the Aztec, who also sometimes carved obsidian jars. It is not possible then to assign these beautiful containers to any one people, place or period. On the other hand, the central Mexican examples have a certain unity, for the shapes either reflect well-known pottery types (Pls. lii and liii) or are effigies representing monkeys (Pl. li), rabbits or jaguars.

SOUTHERN MEXICO

Zapotec and Mixtec cultures. The principal stock of southern Mexico was the Zapotec, whose handiwork can be traced back for many centuries, mainly through excavations in the ruined cities known as Monte Alban and Mitla. The former was one of the truly great aboriginal cities of the New World.

The occupation of Monte Alban has been divided into five principal periods, some of which have been subdivided. The oldest epoch yields remains which are far from primitive, including well made pottery and large stone slabs with engraved figures of dancing men. These obviously are related in style to Olmec art and, in some cases, they bear inscribed dates which have not been deciphered yet. A second period is marked by pre-Classic Maya influence and a third by the development of large and elaborate effigy urns. During the last period of occupation, the Zapotec were superseded at Monte Alban by the Mixtec, who were conquered in 1494 by the Aztec.

The Mixtec were one of the most important Mexican groups in the century before the Spanish conquest. Just where their culture developed is uncertain, but its influence and actual articles of trade reached central Mexico, Yucatan and Guatemala. They produced a highly specialized and delicately painted polychrome pottery with a varnished surface, almost identical in style to the famous Cholula ware, used by Montezuma in his household. Mixtec metalwork represents the finest known craftsmanship in the New World (Pl. lix). The delicacy and skill seen in surviving examples fully bears out the enthusiastic descriptions of the Conquerors. The finest pieces were cast by the *cire perdue* process. This consists of making a wax model, placing it in a clay mold and replacing the wax with molten metal. Filigree objects which appear to be constructed of soldered wire were actually cast as a single unit.

THE MAYA AREA

The Maya, divided into various dialectic groups differing like the Romance languages of Europe, occupied most of Guatemala, adjacent portions of Honduras and El Salvador, all British Honduras, all Yucatan, parts of Campeche and Chiapas. This large area became a cultural unit like Europe through the development of a common architecture, ritualistic symbolism, calendar, hieroglyphic writing system and interchange of articles in trade. This unity, again like Europe, did not blanket regional art styles completely and local developments in architecture, sculpture, pottery, etc. may be noted (fig. 7). No single ruler apparently ever dominated any considerable part of the Maya territory, as is attested by battle scenes in frescoes and bloody wars recorded in legend.

Fig. 7. *Model of a Late Classic Maya temple*. Each tower is in itself a conventionalized temple. Rio Bec, State of Campeche, Mexico. Courtesy American Museum of Natural History.

Beneath the Classic Maya cities are more ancient remains which correspond in cultural plane and also in time to the Archaic period in Mexico. No single center of development can be pointed out, however, and the theory that an 'Old Empire' in Guatemala was deserted to form a 'New Empire' in Yucatan has been abandoned because early occupation has been detected in both.

The rise of the Classic Maya culture was based on the development of their religion, calendar and writing systems in correlation with the discovery of lime mortar and the corbelled vault. This resulted in the erection of large religious centers like Uaxactun, Copan and Tikal and in the development of the stela cult with dated hieroglyphic inscriptions.

Maya buildings are essentially monoliths of rubble and lime with an exterior veneer of cut stone. This outer skin had no structural function but became a field for decoration. Great mosaic faces, frets, false columns and other motifs were built into the walls, or massive carvings in the near round might be attached by projecting tenons. All this once was brilliantly colored, which helped to guide the eye through intricate detail. Much architectural planning clearly was necessary, for, even in a single building, tens of thousands of stones had to be cut to fit their individual places.

Maya art is best known today through the adornment of buildings and through megalithic sculptures. Most of the latter are large rectangular stone columns or stelae, usually with a functionary dressed in ceremonial regalia carved on one side and a hieroglyphic inscription including a date on the opposite side. Sometimes all four sides were carved. This is a flamboyant art, based on serpentine curves which rarely are those of a true circle. It is restless even when the subject is stationary because it is to us so overburdened with detail and because there is a deliberate attempt to avoid any blank spaces. At the same time, this is an aristocratic art, usually executed with assurance and precision, and there is a well developed feeling for balance and symmetry (fig. 8).

The Maya, in their chief bas-relief carving, their frescoes and painted pottery of Late Classic times, often portrayed groups of individuals and various objects with an attempt to show depth and distance. To be sure, other peoples depicted groups but almost invariably they are in a single-file procession. A few crude attempts elsewhere to indicate distance come to mind: Teotihuacan frescoes (Pls. xxv-xxvi), Mixtec codices, Mochica painted pottery, Inca *keros*.

Our linear perspective represents more distant objects as progressively smaller. This optical principle and the mechanics of applying it the Maya did not understand. They habitually represented all individuals of equal social position as equal in size, but they placed more remote figures or objects successively higher in the decorated field. In addition, they employed a, to us, obvious device, the obstructed view, in which a nearer figure partly obscures a more distant one. Thus the Maya were able to convey a sense of distance on flat surfaces, comparable to the isometric projections or geometric elevations traditional in our architectural drawings today.

The Maya did not understand the aerial perspective of our painters, who build up planes of distance by the values of colors, a convention which is ingrained in our sense of perspective.

Fig. 8. *Late Classic Maya stela*. La Amelia, Rio de la Pasion, Dep't of El Peten, Guatemala.
Courtesy Carnegie Institution of Washington.

The aesthetic strivings of the Maya sculptors can be followed on an almost day by day basis during the centuries in which they dated their monuments (fig. 8). The early exuberance of their carving, however, became frozen in stone and, before the end of the Classic period, artists probably were limited in subject matter and ideology by the standing statues of past generations. This stagnation may be compared with most of our own ecclesiastical art and architecture today. Maya art had passed its apogee many centuries before the Spanish conquest, and the 'nuclear classic mode' had been obscured by the introduction of foreign styles.

Apart from monumental sculpture, the Maya produced many small artifacts of shell, bone or stone, including onyx marble and jade. The use of jade extends back to the earliest known pre-Classic pottery periods in Guatemala but the quality of neither the carving nor the stone approaches probably contemporary Olmec specimens. The finest Maya jades – in color, workmanship and size – usually date from the end of the Classic period (Pls. lxv - lxviii).

Maya pottery is complex with many local and chronological variations. The finest pieces of Late Classic times are either carved and incised or are painted in various colors (Pls. lxxix, lxxx, lxxxii, lxxxiii). These vessels evidently were highly prized and were traded over large areas. They frequently show individuals of high rank wearing elaborate costumes and seated on a low throne. Many are adorned with bands of hieroglyphs which rarely fall into the group of inscriptions in stone which has been deciphered. Onyx marble vessels are of great rarity (Pls. lxxxvi and lxxxvii).

Pottery figurines are comparatively rare in the Maya area but there are some specialized local developments. One of these is on the Island of Jaina in the Gulf of Mexico and the adjacent lower course of the Usumacinta River (Pls. lxix-lxxviii). Here large numbers of genre figures have been found, modeled with great skill and in fine detail, often embellished with pastel shades of paint. Although they portray elaboration of dress and adornment, they avoid the flamboyance of ritual Maya art.

The Maya had several methods of recording time. The most accurate of these, like the records of our astronomers, is simply a count of days from a fixed starting point. For nearly six centuries this calendar was in use and the dates are absolute in relation to each other. How to hitch it on to our calendar is not a fully solved problem. Abbreviated dates occur, just as we write '54 for 1954, which often can

be made exact by stylistic associations. The following table shows the divisions of
Maya stylistic development in lowland Guatemala with Maya dates and corresponding dates in our own calendar - as currently accepted. It is possible, however, as a result of recent radiocarbon tests, that the dates in our system should be
set back by about 256 years.

PERIOD	MAYA DATES	OUR DATES
Pre-Classic	? – 8.14.9.0.0	ca. 1000 B.C.–A.D. 306
Early Classic	8.14.9.0.0 – 9.5.0.0.0	A.D. 306–534
Late Classic		
Formative phase	9.8.0.0.0 – 9.13.0.0.0	593–692
Ornate phase	9.13.0.0.0 – 9.16.0.0.0	692–751
Dynamic phase	9.16.0.0 0 – 9.19.0.0.0	751–810
Decadent phase	9.19.0.0.0 – 10.3.0.0.0	810–889

HONDURAS

The Ulua Valley. The plains of Sula in northwestern Honduras are formed by the
adjacent Ulua and Chamelecon rivers. This flat rich valley, today principally
devoted to banana farming, supported a large aboriginal population over a period
of time long enough to permit radical stylistic changes, the result perhaps of
ethnic shifts involving the Maya, Lenca and Paya.

At the time of the Conquest, the Paya lived on the coast east of the Ulua. To
them is attributed a type of tall cylindrical pottery jar with a pair of projecting
handles and incised decoration. In the Ulua region, comparable vessels of white
marble were manufactured with far more precision and skill than is found in the
pottery (Pl. lxxxviii, *top*). The walls usually are completely covered with scroll
patterns delicately executed in relief, sometimes embodying conventionalized
faces.

Until recently, so few of the Ulua marble jars and bowls were known and the
style was so uniform that it was thought a single individual of great talent, or
perhaps a few generations of a single family, might have produced them all.
Today, however, although the Ulua is still believed to have been the manufacturing center, it is recognized that considerable variety in style and skill existed.
Recent excavations indicate exportation to the Comayagua Valley in central

Honduras. Isolated specimens have been found in the Nicoya peninsula in Costa Rica and in Guatemala, which makes it possible to date them from the end of the Maya Late Classic period or shortly thereafter.

COSTA RICA

Nicoya. The Nicoya peninsula forms the northwest corner of Costa Rica. In the sixteenth century, the area was occupied by Indians of Chorotegan stock, related in speech to the Otomí of Mexico. They produced fine polychrome pottery and a large amount of carved jade.

Costa Rican jade usually is a diopside-jadeite, often of a characteristic blue-green color which distinguishes it from Mexican and other Central American jades (Pls. lxxxix, xci, xciii, xciv). About a third of the Nicoya specimens consist of so-called Axe gods, which are pendants the size and shape of a celt, carved to represent men, animals or birds (Pls. xci and xciii). Winged pendants occur (Pl. xci, *top*) which symbolize a bat, the face and body of which sometimes is carved in the center.

Guápiles. This is the name of a modern town in northeastern Costa Rica near which a Chibchan tribe of South American stock once dwelt. This area also became a jade-working center with its own styles and techniques. It also was a center for trade both to the north and south, with the result that it is not easy to determine what was made locally. A lot of the pottery resembles the polychrome ware of Nicoya in northwestern Costa Rica. Gold ornaments occur in considerable quantity and some of the types evidently are local. On the other hand, Coclé and Veraguas styles are frequently found and it has not been determined whether they are imports or local copies.

Jade styles in part are shared with Nicoya but with varying emphasis. Thus the Axe gods form over thirty per cent of the total specimens in Nicoya but only seven per cent in the Guápiles region. Full face figures like the Axe gods are seventy per cent of human or animal forms in Nicoya, while sixty per cent of the Guápiles specimens are in profile. Guápiles jades sometimes reflect the cast gold eagles, frogs or monkeys typical of Coclé and Veraguas in Panama.

Two technical aspects of Guápiles jade are of interest. Tubular beads, thought to have been used by the women to support their breasts, may be as much as fifteen inches long (Pl. xcii, *left*). They were drilled from both ends with the holes meeting almost exactly. This is the deepest drilling of a hard stone yet observed in the New World. The Maya did not drill even half as deep.

Another unusual feature is the common use of string sawing. This consists of coating a string with an abrasive such as sharp sand, emery or pumice and using it to cut. It was no doubt a laborious process because the string wore out and had to be frequently replaced. With this technique, however, it was possible to drill a hole and cut interior lines, often curvilinear, which are typical of Guápiles jades (Pl. xcvi). This process was known by the Olmec and by the Maya of the early Classical period but they rarely used it. The first steel secured by natives of the West Indies, to the surprise of the Spaniards, was cut with string.

PANAMA

In spite of its small size, the Republic of Panama held four distinct material cultures at the time of the Spanish conquest. Physical types varied greatly. The speech consisted of Chibchan dialects so different from each other that interpreters were often needed, but this did not prove a barrier to trade, which was extensive except in time of war.

Coclé culture. This culture flourished in the Province of Coclé and, in modified forms, in the Asuero peninsula, the Pearl Islands and eastward as far as the Panama Canal. This area produced brilliant polychrome pottery and a great variety of jewelry of cast or hammered gold, shell, bone, tooth ivory and such stones as tawny agate, green serpentine, jasper, opal and emerald.

Among the hammered gold artifacts we may mention helmets, cuffs, greaves, socketed ear spools, and breastplates as much as a foot in width (Pls. cviii and cix). Many types of pendants and nose ornaments were cast. The Coclesanos were one of the few aboriginal American groups who habitually made hollow castings in the round over a clay and charcoal core. They also sheathed wood with gold and they placed in cast gold settings such substances as quartz, emerald and carved whale-tooth ivory.

Special manifestations of Coclé culture, notably at Venado Beach in the Canal Zone, include ornaments of shell (Pl. cxii). In many cases these were cut in forms which were produced elsewhere in gold.

Underlying the complex Coclé culture is a simpler and older phase. No metal or polychrome pottery has been found with it.

Veraguas culture. The Province of Veraguas in Panama is adjacent to Coclé on the west. It was a great manufacturing center for cast gold ornaments which were traded in quantity as far as Yucatan and central Mexico. On account of its wealth, the Columbus family selected Veraguas as their Duchy and the title still exists.

Columbus, who discovered Veraguas in 1502, and other early explorers of the Caribbean make frequent reference to gold 'eagles' which were worn as pendants by the natives (Pls. xcvii-xcix). These are particularly abundant in Veraguas, where they were cast as a unit including the filigree details and the flat sheets representing wings and tail. Whether the bird portrayed is or is not an eagle may be argued but they have been thus named for centuries.

Veraguas ornaments also take the form of men, animals, birds and anthropomorphic deities rendered with a wealth of symbolism (Pl. cii). They usually were cast by the *cire perdue* process, not in the round as in Coclé but with open backs. Many specimens are of high grade gold-copper alloy with silver present as an impurity. The surface copper of such pieces was etched away with acid, leaving an outer covering of relatively good gold. The inner cores today often are corroded and brittle.

Apart from metalwork, the natives of Veraguas produced little of interest. Their pottery and stone jewelry were of poor quality, unless imported from Coclé. They ranked with the Araucanians of Chile, however, as the fiercest fighters encountered by the Spaniards.

Chiriquí culture. The Province of Chiriquí lies west of Veraguas and extends to the Costa Rican border. About a century ago, it was discovered that aboriginal graves sometimes contained gold, which resulted in their systematic looting. During the 1860's, the Bank of England melted Chiriquí jewelry to the value of £10,000 annually. Until twenty-five years ago, all Panamanian gold which reached museums was automatically labelled Chiriquí.

A by-product of the gold rush was a vast amount of pottery, which differs in style from the ceramics of Coclé and Veraguas. When first published, it was assumed that the pottery was of local manufacture, but a reappraisal indicates that a lot was imported. Publication of previously unidentified styles of Coclé and

Veraguas gold revealed that over half the Chiriquí gold is in the style of those regions and presumably was imported.

Today, determination of what was manufactured locally is an unsolved problem.

COLOMBIA

Colombia occupies the northwestern portion of South America and is joined to Central America by the Isthmus of Panama. The western third of the country is filled by the peaks and valleys of the Andes which are divided into four principal ranges. Here, it is said, are to be found more different kinds of land than in any comparable area in South America. The geographic diversity had imposed serious barriers to travel before the days of airplanes and fostered the formation of relatively small communities and political units. It has also proved a barrier to archaeological studies and, although for centuries graves have been opened in the search for gold, Colombian pre-history is the least known of any area of relatively high culture in the New World.

In the sixteenth century, the mountain region of Colombia must have possessed a fantastic amount of gold artifacts. Cieza de Leon, one of the *Conquistadores*, wrote in 1547, 'If the gold in the provinces near the great river of Santa Marta (Magdalena), from the city of Popoyan to the town of Mampox, had been in the power of a single lord, as it was in Peru, the wealth would have been greater than that of Cuzco.'

Chibcha style. The Chibcha, dwelling in the vicinity of Bogotá, comprised a number of local chiefs who lived ostentatiously and ceremoniously in houses hung with plates of gold, and they traveled in gold-encased litters. But they had no stone architecture nor large religious or municipal buildings. Their historical memory, at the time of the Conquest, was limited to three generations - about 60 years - and recorded wars of conquest through which neighboring chiefs were made tributary. This may be compared to the early Aztec expansion but definitely did not create a stable political center. The Chibcha did not organize to fight a major battle with the Spaniards but were reduced in a series of local conflicts.

The Chibcha, in comparison with other peoples of Colombia, were technically backward. Their pottery is undistinguished. They did not weave designs in their textiles, but painted them. They did not mine their gold or copper, but secured them in exchange for salt.

To be sure, they shared the metallurgical techniques known elsewhere in Colombia such as wax modeling and surface enrichment of copper-gold alloys. On the other hand, their castings usually are flat sheets with such details as eyes, nose, arms and legs, shields and weapons built up with wax threads. The effect is that of filigree but most castings were made with only one flow of metal (Pl. cxiv, *top left*). The result of this method of manufacture is a two-dimensional effect when portraying subjects which call for three. Aesthetic freedom is sharply limited. Furthermore, the Chibcha rarely burnished their castings but left them rough-surfaced as they came from the mold. This may reveal interesting details of manufacture but does not enhance the aesthetic appeal of their products.

Quimbaya style. One of the most beautiful styles of Colombian metalwork is attributed to the Quimbaya tribe, who occupied a 'province' 10 by 15 leagues in size in the middle Cauca valley. 'The men of this province,' we are told, 'are well disposed, and of good countenances; the women are the same, and very amorous. The houses are small and roofed with reeds of cane . . . They do not eat human flesh, except on very great occasions, and the chiefs alone are very rich in gold.'

It is known that the historic Quimbaya tribe had invaded the region in which the Spanish found them and killed off the previous inhabitants. The suggestion has been made that the archaeological types termed Quimbaya are, in fact, several centuries older than the historic group. We do not agree with this because Spanish eyewitnesses speak of their great gold vases which have been found archaeologically. Also, because in Panama we have excavated Quimbaya trade pieces together with local artifacts which did not long antedate the Conquest.

Quimbaya metalwork usually consists of large massive castings. Bottles and large figurines are typical. Characteristically, they have broad, highly burnished surfaces enhanced by delicately detailed bands which were built up with wax threads, the whole being cast in a single flow of metal.

Darien style. Until recently, the term Quimbaya was applied to a much wider range of artifacts than at present. Need has arisen for a more elaborate classification. As a result various anthropomorphic pendants from the upper Atrato region are now referred to as Darien style. These usually have mushroom-shape ornaments on top of the head and carry two staffs in the hands (Pl. cxvii, *bottom right*).

Conto style. Another local gold style is found around the headwaters of the Colima river in southwestern Colombia. It is distinguished by large gorgets of sheet metal with a human head in the center hammered in high relief. Frequently large cup-like ear ornaments are attached by wires (Pl. cxviii).

Tolima style. Still another stylistic group which formerly has been published as Quimbaya is now known to come from southern Colombia and at present is termed Tolima. The artifacts are rather simple flat castings showing a head, body and limbs, usually in conventionalized simplicity (Pl. cxvii, *top left*). Sometimes a bifurcated tail or wings are added.

VENEZUELA

The early Venezuelans left simple but by no means uniform cultural remains. Gold ornaments were used but have not been found in recorded excavations. The only two published specimens are of similar type and surprisingly ornate. One is said to have come from the vicinity of Maracaibo (Pl. cxix). The style is reminiscent of the Tairona on the north coast of Colombia and both Venezuelan pieces may have been imported.

PERU

Peru is divided into contrasting areas by climate and topography. The eastern portion of the country forms part of the densely forested Amazon basin. The backbone of Peru consists of the three principal ranges of the Andes. The central range, or White Andes, although lacking individual peaks equalling heights to be found in the Himalayas, is considered the highest mountain range in the world. For hundreds of miles almost every crest tops 20,000 feet. Although considerable areas are covered with ice and snow or consist of barren rocks, there are large plateaus and upland valleys suitable for grazing and agriculture. Terracing of mountain sides for agricultural purposes must have begun in the remote past and was perfected with incredible labor. The habitable portions of the mountains thus became densely populated long ago.

The coast of Peru, approximately equal in length to the Pacific seaboard of the United States, is a desert, but the soil is rich and yields abundantly when furnished

with water. The waters of fifty-odd rivers as well as underground flows have
made it possible to support large communities. At the same time, the dryness of
the soil has resulted in the preservation of normally perishable archaeological
materials such as wood, textiles and even feathers.

Archaeological studies cover a span of some 4,000 years before the Spanish
conquest. The earliest settlements reveal only chipped stone tools with animal,
fish and shell-fish remains, but, by about 2500 B.C. agriculture had been established on the coast. Around 1200 B.C. maize, cotton and pottery were in use.

On three separate occasions, local art styles, developed in the mountains, expanded over most or all of Peru. They are known as Chavin, Tiahuanaco and
Inca. Such dispersals of culture, assuming they take place rapidly, offer a means of
cross-dating many geographical areas, progressively less exact as distances increase.
The Chavin expansion probably took place before 700 B.C.

It is difficult to ascertain the causes of cultural expansion in the distant past. In
the case of the Inca, this is no problem because historical records of military conquest exist. The Tiahuanaco dispersal may have been in part the result of force but
it reached such distant lands that we must conclude that it was largely due to
aesthetic appeal. The Chavin expansion, geographically the smallest, may represent the spread of a religious cult and its symbolism. It is doubtful that, at the
period, communities of sufficient size existed to organize widespread conquests.

Coastal Chavin or Cupisnique culture. Chavin culture is named for a massive
and large stone temple in the high Andes, obliterated a few years ago by a landslide. It was adorned with large bas-reliefs and heads in the round attached to the
outer walls. They were carved in a characteristic style, with strong emphasis on
curves at once massive and flowing. Kroeber wrote that 'the type of line and the
load of symbolism carry a suggestion of Maya art, though there is no evidence
of historical connection.' He regarded Chavin as 'the greatest art style evolved in
Peru and in South America' and adds, 'At its best it possesses grandeur, at its worst
it becomes obsessed with the monstrous.'

On the coast, many smaller artifacts of Chavin style have been preserved,
including textiles, pottery and stone vessels (Pl. cxx-cxxi), as well as ornaments
and utensils of bone and gold (Pl. cxxii, *top right, bottom center*). These include
the most ancient metal artifacts south of the United States, where an independent
invention of metalworking had taken place many centuries earlier.

Chavin culture as we now know it has no recognized stylistic antecedents nor has its local starting point been determined. It seems improbable that the style developed in the large and complex sculptures at the type site. At any rate, in other media such as metal, carved bone, pottery, small objects of stone, etc., the style spread over northern and central Peru. It has been detected as far north as Ecuador and to the south as far as Paracas.

Chavin art was largely religious and was dominated by a jaguar deity, usually represented with long curved canine teeth. This god at times assumed the attributes of a bird and is shown with wings and a mask shaped like the head of a vulture or condor in front of the feline head. Like the Aztec Rain god Tlaloc, the Chavin deity had an affinity with serpents, which may be shown issuing from his mouth or framing the face.

Mochica culture. In northern Peru after the full flowering of Chavin, there followed two periods of relative cultural poverty, known as Salinar and Gallinazo, during which the art of metallurgy became almost extinct on the north coast while pottery of inferior design and quality was manufactured. About A.D. 100 there took place a strong revival in all the arts, accompanied by the introduction of new styles. Thus was initiated what is called the Mochica period.

This sequence of cultures is well established by stratigraphic excavations, but, in a few coastal valleys, Chavin ceramic styles persisted in very small quantity, apparently for several centuries. A few examples of typical Chavin pottery have been found in graves as recent as the Mochica period. It seems then that certain aspects of Chavin may have existed for a full millennium and that sub-styles or phases will have to be determined and arranged chronologically.

Although the Mochica styles are confined to a few coastal valleys, there is such a vast quantity of archaeological material available for study that it has been possible to gain a detailed view of this complex and vigorous Peruvian culture. One of the great accomplishments of Mochica was the introduction of several new pottery types. Life forms, modeled as pottery vessels, had previously been produced for some time with mediocre success but there now was a tremendous development, accompanied by the manufacture of jars with elaborate scenes painted on their walls. As a result, almost every human activity from birth to death was pictured in a style of great vigor and freshness.

Metalworking also expanded. The use of copper and copper tools became common. Casting, gilding and silvering were discovered.

The Mochica era evidently lasted for many centuries. Several phases represented by stylistic changes have been recognized, and their influence persisted until the Spanish conquest.

Turning to southern Peru, we find coastal cultures contemporaneous with those we have pictured in the north. The oldest known settlements had no pottery or agriculture but again agriculture appeared before pottery.

Paracas styles. The first advanced period of the south was a brilliant one, named for the Paracas peninsula south of Pisco. Here were found deep bottle-neck tombs with very unusual pottery types (Paracas-Cavernas) and mummy bundles with exquisite textiles buried in small houses (Paracas-Necropolis).

The Paracas-Necropolis weaving includes many types of garments and almost all Peruvian weaving techniques. Designs are boldly executed in brilliant colors of many shades. Among the outstanding fabrics are large shawls of cotton with wool embroidered borders and the central field filled with repeated rows of human or animal figures, related in style to Nazca pottery.

The suggestion has been made that the Paracas people lived in the mountains and came to the coast only to fish or bury their dead - in the Pisco, Ocucaje and Nazca valleys. It is indeed true that proper housing for such a brilliant culture has not been found near the coast, but no trace of it has been detected in the mountains. At present, the Paracas peninsula and southern part of the Pisco valley form an arid sand desert, but the water table is only a few feet down. Occasional patches of struggling vegetation suggest that, until recently, large areas might have been in cultivation.

Nazca styles. The earliest Nazca remains occur in the Ica and Nazca valleys in southern Peru. They are marked by a high development of polychrome pottery which falls into several phases. Modeled forms are comparatively rare. Some of the painted designs are semi-realistic portrayals of men, birds, animals and fish. Many anthropomorphic deities also appear, often in exaggerated and flamboyant forms. During a second phase, new designs were introduced and the complexity of both pattern and color was increased. This was followed by a third style marked by simplified degeneration of design and cruder workmanship, in part contemporaneous with the Tiahuanaco expansion, to be discussed presently. The last two phases of Nazca witnessed a geographical expansion along the coast, northward to the Asia Valley and south beyond the Majes Valley.

A few pieces of sheet metal, consisting of hammered silver or gold nuggets, were found at Paracas. Nazca also produced metalwork of this type, as well as larger and more elaborate forms in beaten gold. Casting began in the Nazca region shortly before the art style terminated but never became common anywhere on the south coast.

Tiahuanaco styles. The classic style known as Tiahuanaco is named for a ruined city, over 13,000 feet above sea level on the Bolivian plateau, which contains a large amount of sculpture, mostly in flat relief. This city, however, probably was not the center where the style developed, for the motifs carved in stone seem to be taken from textile or pottery designs.

Tiahuanaco art is highly conventional and formalized. It portrays condors and jaguars, running figures in profile with a cape, men full-face holding a staff in each hand. Among typical details, we may mention square heads, weeping or winged eyes, N-shaped incisor teeth (Pl. cl), appendages in the form of puma, fish or condor heads, three-fingered hands (Pl. cxlv).

Probably about A.D. 700 the Tiahuanaco style spread all over Peru in surprisingly pure form. Local components soon were added but some of the detailed traits can be noted in archaeological remains from such distant lands as Argentina and Chile, Panama and Costa Rica. There is no positive indication of conquest or political expansion, which would have been physically and geographically impossible in the case of the more remote areas. Apparently various aspects of the Tiahuanaco styles appealed to the aesthetic concepts of several million aboriginal Americans in many communities and therefore were copied or adapted to local art forms.

The time element obviously is important. Dispersal in Peru may have taken place rapidly, and it put an end to many local styles such as Mochica and Nazca. It is not safe, however, to assume that all aspects of Tiahuanaco outside the homeland in the south are approximately contemporaneous. It can be demonstrated that the Tiahuanaco influence in Panama and southern Costa Rica dates from just before the Spanish conquest.

Post-Tiahuanaco late coastal styles. After the pan-Peruvian wave of Tiahuanaco influences receded, local art styles either were revived in modified form or new

Fig. 9. *Inca masonry*. Top: Temple of the Sun, Cuzco. Bottom: Sacsahuaman fortress, outside Cuzco.
Courtesy American Museum of Natural History.

ones were created. The use of metal, including copper, bronze, gold, silver and lead, became common. Textiles tend to geometric patterns, even when depicting life forms such as men, birds or fish. Pottery tends towards less fluid lines and decreasing use of color.

Chimu. This is the name of a culture developed on the north coast under the Chimu dynasty, who ruled in Chanchan, generally considered the largest city of aboriginal America. Just how far their political power extended is not known. Their stylistic influence has been detected from the Chira in the north to the Casma Valley in the south and beyond.

The Chimu revived much of the Mochica art tradition but practised new techniques such as the casting of bronze. Their art, however, lacks the freshness and vigor of earlier times, due perhaps to increased production of identical forms in molds. Nevertheless, many of their tools and household utensils of wood or bronze have great charm, and the textiles, better preserved than those of earlier ages, often are magnificent.

Chancay. The Chancay culture of the central coast around Lima produced a great deal of metalwork and fine textiles. The pottery, however, is mostly of poor quality. Decoration is limited to black line patterns, cream or simple white patterns with black outlines on red and molded designs in relief.

Ica. After the Tiahuanaco infiltration, the polychrome tradition in pottery continued to flourish on the south coast in styles named for the Ica and Chinca valleys but fewer colors were employed. Fine textiles continued to be manufactured. The use of metals, however, did not become common except for hammered ornaments. Cast artifacts of any kind are rare.

Inca culture. The Inca, as the conquerors of Peru and adjacent lands, were the masters of all arts and skills in their domain. They were, however, fine craftsmen in their own right, working in what we may call the School of Cuzco. Their buildings are noted for the beauty of their masonry (fig. 9), but they did not produce large stone statuary. Some of their small carvings, especially stone bowls and cups, were very fine. Their weaving definitely was of top rank (Pls. clxi and clxii). The Inca arts and artifacts were spread as the result of conquest and may be expected to turn up wherever their troops or officials were stationed. Local pottery often incorporates ingredients of the Inca styles.

In history the Inca are famous for their metalwork: its abundance, the size of individual objects and also the delicacy of the workmanship. Rooms sheathed in gold, temples with gold friezes, life-size statues and huge vessels have been described, also delicately wrought gardens of golden maize and butterflies so thin that they fluttered in the wind. This opulence the Spanish conquerors described in detail but it has all disappeared in the melting pot. Excavations have produced small hollow figurines of gold and silver representing men, women and llamas (Pl. cxxxv). Also, copper and bronze tools, utensils, and weapons have been found, such as pins, ear spoons and knives (Pls. cxxxii and cxxxiii). The Inca made only one contribution to Peruvian metallurgy: the inlaying of metal with other metals (Pls. cxxxvi and cxxxvii).

At present, archaeologists recognize over sixty different styles, periods or phases of culture in Peru. This diversity represents both time and space. On the other hand, the three pan-Peruvian periods were unifying forces, and the Peru which the Spaniards conquered should be regarded as a single unit of culture with such local modifications as are to be expected in a large nation.

October 20, 1954

MINERALOGICAL ATTRIBUTIONS
by W. F. Foshag

MINERALOGICAL ATTRIBUTIONS

AN EXAMINATION of any comprehensive collection of pre-Hispanic indigenous American fine-stone carving or sculpture demonstrates that even the earliest known lapidaries no longer relied upon the common materials that were readily at hand for the stone they wished to elaborate, but that they sought out the most appropriate materials, even from distant areas. Only fine materials attracted them and the artist demanded stones of merit such as jade, turquoise and rock crystal. Among these minerals were some of the most refractory nature, to fashion which invoked his highest skills. Not only were his materials hard and tough, but often rare, so that he had to seek them out in a few favored places or acquire them by trade or tribute from remote regions.

The early lapidary worked with the simplest of implements, chiefly of stone, but supplemented by others of wood, reed, bone and rawhide. He had no metal tools, except as a very late Spanish introduction. With his stone tools he ground, pecked, rasped, sawed, drilled, reamed and polished, as well as incised and engraved. Nor did he have ultra-hard abrasives, but used material no harder than the stone he fashioned, using the principle of 'diamond cut diamond'. He understood the particular attributes of each variety of stone, and by the most primitive of lapidary techniques he elaborated objects of the highest artistic merit.

The Meso-American artist used jade, turquoise, serpentine, obsidian, rock crystal, onyx marble, diorite and a number of lesser stones. The South American lapidary was not so skilled as his northern neighbor, and more restricted in variety of stone, but he had access to emeralds of the finest quality.

Jade is a generic term used to designate several distinct mineral species widely used in primitive cultures for such simple utilitarian objects as celts or knives, and in more advanced civilizations for such decorative pieces as jewels, ceremonial objects and carvings.

The word jade was derived from the Spanish term *piedra de ijada,* or 'stone of the loin', in allusion to the virtue imputed to it of relieving pains of the side or of the kidneys. From the word jade was derived the specific name jadeite, applied to the pyroxenic mineral that constitutes one form of jade. The Spanish term, when translated into Latin, became *lapis nephriticus,* from which was derived the

45

name *nephrite,* now used to designate a second mineralogical variety of jade. Thus, two distinct mineral species became associated with the term jade: jadeite (and its congeners diopside-jadeite and chloromelanite) and nephrite.

Jadeite was used by all the advanced cultures of Meso-America. Among the Aztec it was known as *chalchihuitl* and was considered the most precious of stones. An indication of the great value put upon it by them was expressed by Montezuma, who, in presenting several jade ornaments to Cortés, told him: 'I will give you some very valuable stones, which you will send to him in my name; they are chalchihuitls and are not to be given to any one else but to him, your great Prince. Each stone is worth two loads of gold.'

Although Meso-American jadeite is similar to the Asiatic mineral that we know so well today, it shows significant chemical differences and a much wider variety in color and texture. In addition to the pure species, jadeite, two varieties, diopside-jadeite and chloromelanite, not found in oriental forms, are represented in the American material.

The finest quality of oriental jadeite is known to the Chinese as *fei-t'sui,* or kingfisher jade, in allusion to its rich green color, not unlike the color of that Chinese bird. Its color is emerald green; its dense body texture yields a diaphaniety almost crystalline; and its luster on a polished surface is pearly. This supreme variety of jade is also found among Meso-American objects, and, like the Chinese stone, only in small and rare pieces. It was known to the Aztec as *quetzalitztli,* its rich color suggesting the vivid green of the plumage of the quetzal.

Similar to quetzalitzli but lacking its diaphaniety was the *quetzal-chalchuitl,* or 'quetzal jade', a rich green stone sometimes found among the finer Olmecan pieces. The commoner chalchuitl was green mottled with white, indistinguishable from much of the Asiatic green jade seen in today's markets (Pl. xxix, No. 37). *Iztacchalchuitl,* or white jade, is the same stone with little or no coloration.

A second distinct variety of jadeite is pale celadon or siskin green and uniformly colored. It sometimes shows a very marked, coarse granular structure, or the granularity may be indistinct and the luster somewhat waxy. It is found chiefly in highland Mayan objects, such as the flat carved faces characteristic of that culture (Pls. lxvii and lxv, *upper right* and *center)* or, more rarely, as Aztecan carved discs and simple ear-plugs or Costa Rican long tubular beads (Pl. xcii, *left).*

A distinct and striking variety of jadeite is compact, without apparent grain, somewhat translucent, its color ranging from pale greenish- or bluish-gray through all nuances to dark ivy-green, dark blue-gray to almost black. It is frequently speckled with white, ghostlike spots within the body of the stone. This form of jadeite was a favorite material of the Olmecan artist (Pls. iii and ix, *bottom*), and almost the only variety known to the Nicoyans of Costa Rica.

Diopside-jadeite is a mineralogical variety of jadeite usually difficult to differentiate from the chemically purer form. Since it is the material of the famous Tuxtla statuette (Smithsonian Institution), it is sometimes referred to as *tuxtlite*. The stone, although often of an attractive green, usually lacks the purity of hue of jadeite (Pl. lv).

Chloromelanite is a second mineralogical variety of jadeite. As its name suggests, it is very dark green to almost black in color. This is probably the Aztec stone *tlilayotic*, a name that may be translated 'dark green gourd-color stone'. It was widely used for celts and similar utilitarian objects, even as early as pre-Classic cultures, and occasionally for works of artistic merit.

Nephrite, the densely matted and tough form of the amphibole minerals tremolite or actinolite, and the second mineralogical species included within the term jade, has not been found in Meso-American carvings. A compact form of tremolite, lacking the reticulated structure and tough nature of true nephrite, forms the stone of the handsome Olmecan mask shown in Pl. vi, *center*. Nephrite is found widely distributed in South America in the form of simple utilitarian celts.

Turquoise was a stone highly prized by the Aztec and was also favored by the Tarascan. It was used sparingly in other cultures of South and Meso-America. In South America it was used as early as Chavin times (700 B.C.). To the Aztec it was known as *xiuhuitl* and, the finest quality, as *teoxiuhuitl,* or 'turquoise of the gods'. Its use was restricted to the gods, the king and the nobles. The kings' mark of rank was the *xiuhuitzolli,* or turquoise mitre.

Apparently, turquoise was rare in both South and Meso-America, for it was usually cut into thin plates to yield the maximum surface and used in this form in mosaics, or as inlay in gold and shell (Pl. cxxvii). Skulls, masks and shields, inlaid with hundreds of small turquoise plates, are among the most striking and rarest examples of Aztecan and Mixtec art (Pl. lx). A treasured ornament of Aztec kings was a delicately carved turquoise nose-plug of the finest quality stone.

The early indigenous source of turquoise is now unknown. Towns in Guerrero and Vera Cruz paid tribute in turquoise to Montezuma. Fray Sahagun tells us that it came from distant mines. It is probable that the stone reached the Aztec from the ancient mines in New Mexico that supplied the cultures of south-western United States with the mineral as early as the twelfth century.

Due to its rarity, the early lapidaries sought for substitutes for turquoise and found it, to a limited extent, in the blue or green form of feldspar called amazon-stone. Like turquoise, it was used in mosaics. The highland Maya also fashioned small beads of it.

Serpentine is a mineral having a dull gray-green color and a compact aphanitic texture (Pl. iv and v). A rare form of it, fine apple- to dark-green, and translucent, is classed among the gem stones and is called precious serpentine or *williamsite.* Intermediate between the dull common stone and precious serpentine are grades of light to dark green, capable of retaining a good polish and which, when worked into figurines, are sometimes difficult to distinguish from some of the darker forms of jade. Some of the finest accomplishments of Olmecan artists are in this stone, particularly figurines (Pl. iv and v). Unusually fine examples of Teotihuacan masks in this material have also been found (Pl. xxviii). Except for the Olmecan and Teotihuacanan artists, other artists used the stone for lesser objects only. Serpentine is found in the States of Puebla and Vera Cruz, Mexico, and in Guatemala.

Soapstone is a soft compact mineral, not unlike serpentine, but softer in nature, and easily worked. Its usual color is pale gray or grayish buff. It was used extensively by the highland Maya for the manufacture of beads, but was seldom elaborated into important works of art. Unusual pieces of particularly even color and texture, however, seemed to have engaged the fancy of the artist, and yielded works of considerable artistic merit, usually in the form of vases, beakers or bowls, with sculptured design (Pl. cxx).

Obsidian is a natural volcanic glass, a rapidly congealed form of lava. It was known to the Aztec as *itztli.* It breaks with a perfect conchoidal fracture so that the stone, broken in a manner well developed by the native artisan, yielded sharp, razor-like edges. For this reason it served not only for arrow points, spearheads and razors, but also for the terrible *maquauitl,* or obsidian-edged swords with which the warrior slew his enemy. The priests, however, found the stone too brittle for the knives with which they sacrificed their victims to the gods, preferring the lesser edged but tougher *tecpatl*, or flint.

Obsidian was also used in the finer arts, carved into masks or figures, of which the skull was the most popular motif (Pl. xlvii). It was the favorite stone for *nacochtli*, or spool-shaped ear-plugs, worked to a paper thinness, an astounding accomplishment of the native lapidaries (Pl. l, Nos. 68, 71 and 72).

Three colors of obsidian were used: a grayish-black, a vitreous pitchy-black and a dark olive-green of unusual vitreosity. The pitchy-black stone was used extensively for 'top-hat'-shaped labrets, the finer green variety for ear-plugs.

A number of localities in Meso-America yielded obsidian. An important mining center for the stone was the Cerro de las Nevajas (Hill of the Knives), in the State of Hidalgo, Mexico.

Emerald is the rich green form of the mineral beryl. Before the Spaniards discovered the mines in Colombia in 1544, the principal sources of the gem were the inferior grades from the mines in Egypt and Austria. The Inca in Peru, and the Muzo and Chibcha in Colombia, and even earlier cultures in Ecuador, knew this stone and many fine crystals were obtained as loot by Pizarro and his freebooting followers. It is doubtful that the stone was elaborately worked other than by drilling the rough crystals for beads or fashioning simple cabochons, for the superior hardness (8 on the Mohs scale) probably defied the simple techniques of the lapidary. Fray Torquemada tells us that the stone was mounted in gold. Since the crystals as they come from the mines have good natural, lustrous facets, it is probable that many were used without elaboration.

The early chronicles of New Spain frequently referred to the fine green stones used by the Aztec as 'esmeralda' (emerald). Because no source of the gem is known in Meso-America, and none have been found at archaeological sites in that region north of Panama, it is probable that they referred to the finer qualities of jade, some examples of which surpassed in beauty the inferior emeralds then known to them.

Prehnite is a green stone resembling some form of jade. A high polish can be imparted to it, which, like that of jade, will resist the ravages of time. In its natural occurrence it is sometimes associated with copper, and minute flakes of that metal within the body of the stone are sufficient to identify it. Beads of this mineral are not uncommon in some parts of Mexico, but fine carvings in this stone are rare (Pl. lviii, *bottom left*. No. 94).

Rock crystal is the transparent, colorless form of the common mineral quartz. It was known to the Aztec as *teuhuitl* or *chipilotl*. The amethystine-colored form of rock crystal, amethyst, was also known to them as *tlapalteuhuitl*, or red rock crystal. As far as we now know, rock crystal was worked into elaborate sculptural forms only by the Aztec, although unpolished crystals and simple pendants of this stone were used by the highland Maya of Guatemala, and bead necklaces have been found on the north coast of Peru.

This mineral is harder than steel, and extremely difficult to work; nevertheless, the Aztec artists were able to fashion it into sculptural forms of great merit. Carvings in the form of skulls were particularly favored (Pl. xlviii, *top center*. No. 62). It was often used in labrets and ear-plugs, sometimes mounted with gold (Pl. l. Nos. 69 and 70).

A curious use, described by Fray Sahagun, was in the form of hollow tubes and labrets, into which blue feathers were introduced, so that the stone simulated sapphire.

Onyx marble is a fine-grained form of marble deposited about springs. Usually the layered nature of the stone is apparent in the banded structure, implied in its name. It is erroneously called alabaster, because it resembles that stone, but onyx marble is somewhat harder.

The stone was known to the Aztec as *tecali*, and was mined by them and earlier people at several localities in the State of Puebla, Mexico. The finest quality, translucent, and pale apple-green in color, undoubtedly came from what is now known as the Pedrara quarry in the district of Tecali, and was used in Teotihuacan masks (Frontispiece and Pl. xxx, *top*, No. 38). A white, semi-translucent, banded stone, perhaps from the Sorpresa quarry west of Antigua Salinas, was carved by the Mexicans into urns (Pls. li, lii, liii, lxxxvi, lxxxvii).

Marble, of the more ordinary form, some not unlike the Carrara marble of Italy, was used in Olmecan masks (Pl. vii), and Totonac ceremonial carved celts and palmate stones (Pls. xiv, xvii, xxii), and Teotihuacan masks (Pl. lvi).

Diorite and *metadiorite* are two common rock forms, dark gray, green or black in color (Pls. xlii-xlv, Nos. 56, 57, 58). Diorite is made up chiefly of two minerals: a light one, feldspar; and a dark one, pyroxene, so that the coarser-grained forms often have a speckled appearance. Metadiorite is a form of diorite which has, as a result of geologic metamorphism, acquired a mottled green color of pleasing aspect. It is often mistaken for jade, which it sometimes resembles, but it lacks the vivid hue and will not assume, when polished, the pearly luster of that mineral. The fine-grained texture of both diorite and metadiorite permitted the artist to exercise his skill in the elaboration of complicated forms such as the two maceheads (Pls. xc, *center;* cxxi, *bottom*). The figure of Xipe (Pl. xlv) is an outstanding example of sculpture in this stone.

There are other stones of merit used occasionally for minor objects, simple pendants or small figurines. The cryptocrystalline forms of quartz: chalcedony, agate, sard, carnelian and bloodstone were used for pendants and particularly for the so-called *pulidores,* or polishers, which were usually fashioned in some form of quartz. Opal was known to the Aztec as *huitzitziltecpatl,* or 'humming-bird jasper'. The Inca knew the lapis-lazuli from the Andes of Ovalle, Chile, and the similar blue sodalite from Cerro Sapo, Bolivia. Specular hematite and pyrite, being metallic minerals capable of receiving a high, reflecting polish, were used as mirrors by the Aztec and many other peoples.

For their larger and more monumental sculptures, the indigenous artist preferred the dark red or black lava called basalt, particularly the somewhat porous form that the Aztec called *tezontli.* This rock, although hard, yielded readily to the artist's simple tools (Pls. xxxv, *left;* xx).

TEXTILES

by Joy Mahler

TEXTILES

ALL textiles in the collection come from the coastal area of Peru, famous for prehistoric cloth of infinite variety in design, color and weaving techniques. The unusually dry coastal climate - there has not been a real rain near Lima since 1925 - is responsible for the preservation for centuries of perishable material, either in burials or as accumulated refuse. Probably the oldest surviving fabrics in the entire world, dating from ca. 2500 B.C., were unearthed on the Peruvian north coast. Doubtless many other American areas achieved a high degree of proficiency in weaving. For instance, from Spanish accounts, as well as from observation of native frescoes, sculpture and codices, we have indirect evidence of other flourishing textile centers. Unfortunately, virtually no tangible examples exist today.

The earliest Peruvian textiles, made in a period prior to the introduction of pottery, were primarily twined rather than woven, of cotton yarn and a spun fiber of the milkweed family. Native cotton, as far as anyone knows, is of the species *Gossypium barbadense,* which ranges in color from white to dark brown. The only other major fiber available in Peru for spinning yarn, which came into use at a later time, was wool from the closely related cameloids, the domesticated llama and alpaca, or the wild vicuña.

Camel hair has long been known for its texture. Of all the cameloids, vicuña is noted especially for its unsurpassed softness, and it is in fact the finest of any known animal, with a count of about 2500 hairs to the inch. The smallest of the American camels, it lives as high as 16,000 feet in the Andes. It is completely wild, and, unlike its relatives, the alpaca and llama, cannot be raised in captivity but must be killed to be sheared. It is estimated that to secure wool for a modern coat, 40 animals must be killed. Vicuña wool has always been reserved for wealthy aristocrats. In Inca times, this animal was hunted only once in every 4 years. Only selected males were killed and the wool restricted to the Inca clans. In earlier times under less highly organized governments, there probably were no restrictions on hunting vicuña, and the wool probably was traded to the coast.

Wool varies in quality with the age of the animal and the portion of the body from which it comes. Hence positive identification of the different Peruvian wools has rarely ever been made conclusively in individual prehistoric fabrics, and it is virtually impossible to do so without special training. Furthermore, it involves some damage to the cloth by the removal of the necessary quantity of fibers. Thus for this collection no purely speculative attempt has been made to distinguish the species. It is quite possible that mixed wools were used.

In the most outstanding Peruvian textiles, wool and cotton were spun into yarns of such extremely fine quality that they cannot be reproduced today by mechanical spinning apparatus. This amazing skill in spinning was equalled by excellence in dyeing, so that articles made 500 or even many more years ago may still show no evidence of fading. One need only glance at the plates in this volume to be impressed by the great range and brilliance of color.

Perhaps the most remarkable feature is the weaving. Of all the techniques known today the majority were long ago mastered by the ancient Peruvians, who, moreover, accomplished some variations which cannot be manufactured on our modern machine looms. Even in this small select series of 32 examples here illustrated, there are no less than 15 distinct weaves and supplementary techniques. These are discussed in the analyses of each specimen and under Definitions of Terms (p. 57).

By the time the textile craft was fully established in Peru (ca. 700 B.C.), we assume that in all areas practically all techniques were known. However, not infrequently there seem to have been preferences, at least among the ruling classes, for specific weaves. Best known is the emphasis placed on plain weaves embellished with elaborate embroidery in the Paracas-Necropolis burial bundles (Pl. cxli) and on tapestry in the later Tiahuanaco (Pl. cxlvii) and Inca (Pls. clxi, clxii) styles.

Regardless of the manner of weaving, textiles were always completely finished loom products, for garments were not cut and tailored, but were woven to size. Tunics, or poncho shirts, for instance, often consisted of only one cloth. A slit for the neck opening was left during the process of weaving, and later the sides were sewn together below the arm openings. This can be seen in the Inca poncho shirts (Pls. clxi, clxii). Sometimes two pieces were sewn side by side to form a shirt, as in the Tiahuanaco examples seen in Pls. cxliv and cxlvii. In both the Tiahuanaco and Inca tapestries shown in this volume, the warp runs horizontally on the finished fabric. This means that twice the length of the tunics is the actual loom width. Some are surprisingly wide for a hand loom - over 6 feet as in the case of Pl. cxliv.

Many Paracas garments are made of as many as six separately constructed units, four of which are complete loom products. The mantle in Pl. cxli consists of a base fabric of two pieces joined lengthwise at the center. The borders are separately woven, stitched to the sides of the central field, and subsequently embroidered. Finally, the fringes, again individually produced, were applied to the border.

Another interesting feature of some Paracas burial bundles is the matching of garments - poncho shirts, mantles, kilts and turbans all being decorated with identical designs and colors. This has not as yet been reported elsewhere.

The dating of most Peruvian textile material has for the most part been guess-work based on resemblances to stylistic traits of other cultural remains. Despite large numbers of Peruvian collections, these have usually been obtained from looted cemeteries, and lack pottery association and provenance. However, with continued compilation of information, it is becoming apparent that regional differences in technical details as well as in designs will eventually provide safe diagnostics for placing individual specimens exactly in time and area. We can now say, however, that the textiles in this volume cover a period approximately from the third century B.C. to the Spanish conquest and that they represent at least seven major styles.

The pieces have been collected not to show regional and historical sequence of styles but essentially for their individual aesthetic appeal: for their designs and superb blending of colors. The designs themselves represent a mythology and symbolism which are foreign to us but must have conveyed exact meanings to their makers.

DEFINITIONS OF TERMS

Warp Stripe: difference in color of warp yarns produces stripes in the warp.

Weft Stripe: difference in color of weft yarns produces stripes in the weft.

Warp or Weft Pattern: the floating of any given number of yarns over more than one warp or weft to create the design.

Transposed Warp Pattern: the warps temporarily are shifted from their normal vertical position, one or more places to the right or left, thus showing diagonally on the cloth.

Interlocked Warp and Weft: requires the setting up of the warp, usually in contrasting colors, over scaffold yarns, in the pattern of the final fabric. Warps are interlocked and the scaffold yarns may be removed. Weft yarns, in each area generally the same color as those of the warp, are also interlocked at points of color change.

Tapestry: a fabric in which the weft yarns of a given color or pattern unit are restricted to those areas rather than passing from side selvage to side selvage as in plain weaving.

   (a) Slit Tapestry: wefts are not joined at contrasting color areas, but leave slits in the fabric running with the warp.

   (b) Interlocked Tapestry: wefts are turned about one another or about a common warp at contrasting color areas.

   (c) Eccentric Tapestry: wefts are beaten down at angles other than perpendicular to the warp in order to produce curved lines.

Brocade: supplementary weft yarns used in design areas during weaving of the fabric.

Embroidery: supplementary yarns used for decoration after completion of the woven fabric.

One faced: a term applying to a textile finished on one side only. This feature is not always observable in this collection since most fabrics are sewn securely to a mount.

Spinning: the terms Z-spun or S-spun refer to the direction of twist in a yarn. In a Z-spun yarn the angle of twist, when viewed vertically, is from the upper right to the lower left.

Counts: these refer to the relative number of warp and weft yarns in one inch.

Heading Data: these indicate the method of finishing off the warp ends. In Peruvian fabrics, there is seldom any special treatment of the sides, so no mention is given of this feature unless an exception occurs.

Size of Specimens: in addition to the overall dimensions of the garments, the size and number of the loom products is given. With the latter, length is consistently warp length, and width is loom width. When a specimen is fragmentary, the length, even if this is the shorter dimension, is that of the warps, and width is that of the wefts.

NEW WORLD METALLURGY
by S. K. Lothrop

NEW WORLD METALLURGY

KNOWLEDGE of metals did not spread from a single source in the New World. Most aboriginal Americans who had access to virgin metals made some use of them – from the Eskimo in the far north to the Yaghan near Cape Horn. Iron in the form of hematite or pyrites was shaped by abrasive stone-working processes but the other metals used by Indians are those we class as ductile: namely gold, silver, copper, tin, lead and platinum. Analyses reveal that these metals rarely occur in pure form in nature but the presence or absence of other elements, even in minute quantities, may have a radical effect on the quality of the principal metal: its hardness, malleability, annealing point and melting point. No doubt, observant natives took advantage of these intrinsic qualities in local ores.

A conscious alloy of two or more metals obviously is made because the mixture has some advantage over the basic elements. Hardness or malleability may be desirable qualities to primitive people, achieved by alloys as well as cold hammering and annealing. Color also may be an important factor.

Several simple alloys have the practical advantage of a lower melting point than the original elements, a discovery apparently made in Colombia. For instance copper added to gold in a proportion of 18 to 82 lowers the melting point nearly 25 per cent. Anywhere from 5 to 40 per cent copper with gold lowers the melting point appreciably – at least 100° C. Some Indians, for instance in the Guianas and southern Costa Rica, could melt neither gold nor copper unless the two metals were powdered and combined.

The discovery of this copper-gold alloy, known as *tumbaga,* is believed to have taken place in Colombia because most cast objects from that country are made of it. The event took place well over 1,000 years ago, and knowledge of the alloy spread to Peru, Mexico and the West Indies.

Tumbaga has two additional qualities which were known to the natives. First, by a combination of heating and soaking in acid, surface copper was removed, leaving a skin of gold which could be renewed if it wore away. This process, known as surface enrichment or *mise en couleur,* is not a true gilding because no metal is added. Secondly, by annealing and hammering, *tumbaga* can be made nearly as hard as bronze or soft steel. Aboriginal Americans then possessed a metal useful alike for adornment or cutting tools, not subject to corrosion except through electrolysis, which only occurs in buried archaeological specimens.

One more point about *tumbaga*. When a metal object is heated a dull red, a change in the crystal structure may take place. This is known as annealing or tempering. It usually is done to make the metal less brittle when it is to be hammered. Annealing softens copper and silver but it hardens *tumbaga* and bronze. This contrary reaction must have puzzled the Indian metallurgists.

Most of our 'gold' jewelry today is about 14 carat or less than 60 per cent pure gold. Just what goes into 14 carat gold usually is a trade secret, the object being to produce a metal which looks like gold, is much harder but is not brittle. We have seen figures representing modern French jewelers who use a combination of gold, copper and silver in quantities which are very close to the *tumbaga* alloys.

Other American alloys include copper and tin, combined to make bronze. In Peru bronze was of two qualities, one with a low tin content, suitable for tools as it could be hardened by hammering, one with a high tin content which resulted in more brittle but cleaner castings and therefore was preferred for ornaments. Only the first type of bronze was known in Mexico.

There are two other less well known alloys. One was a silver-copper combination, manufactured for a few centuries before the Conquest in Peru. The silver on the surface sometimes was enriched by removing copper with acid in the same fashion as the copper-gold alloy was treated. In Mexico there was a copper-lead alloy, apparently invented by the Aztec and used for casting small bells at a comparatively low temperature.

Simple castings can be made in open molds, but more complex forms call for closed molds. The typical New World castings were achieved by the so-called lost wax process, which apparently was invented in Colombia and spread with knowledge of the *tumbaga* alloy. Essentially this process consists of making a wax replica, encasing it in a mold of fine clay and charcoal with proper vents, and then replacing the wax with molten metal.

There are various complications, however. For instance, hollow castings can be made by building the wax model over a central core of clay, the whole being encased in an outer mold. Wax sheets of paper thinness were made with rollers on small blocks of well polished stone or metal (Pl. cxxxii, No. 325). Also slim wax threads were coiled or braided in various fashions or combined to seem like soldered filigree. When a section of this is placed under a microscope, however, one can see that no solder is present and the grain structure of the metal is uniform.

The finest lost wax castings come from Colombia, Panama and Costa Rica and from the Aztec and Mixtec regions in Mexico. The delicacy of some of the workmanship is almost beyond belief, but the craftsmanship lay not only in the modelling but in so designing it that the metal would flow to all parts of the mold. In collections such as are exhibited in museums, one sees only the finest pieces, but in any large unselected collection you will find imperfect castings which illustrate the technical problems encountered by the aboriginal goldsmiths.

Although metal was used sporadically all over the Americas, there were comparatively few areas where it was in common use. The oldest of these centers, as determined by radiocarbon dates, started at least 3,500 years ago in the Great Lakes region in the United States, where massive tools were hammered from copper nuggets, presumably with the aid of annealing. This apparently is the only case in the entire world where the use of metal preceded the use of pottery. This North American metallurgical industry gradually spread over the eastern half of the continent but did not penetrate to Mexico. No metal was ever melted. The only technological advances were the art of sheathing other materials, for which occasionally gold and silver nuggets were used as well as copper, and the manufacture of elaborate and sometimes very beautiful ornaments by trimming and embossing hammered copper sheets.

We have then a curious phenomenon in North America: the discovery of metal and also a simple process for working it which remained nearly static for about 3,000 years. It is curious that the discovery of metals was not made in our western States. We have read of a gold nugget found in California which was four and one-half feet long and weighed 2,340 ounces, or nearly 150 pounds. We are surprised that some Indian did not keep such a glittering object and learn that he could not chip it, but could pound it to shape. If a house burned down in a high wind, you would discover that metal will melt if there is enough heat. These seemingly logical events, however, never took place.

Turning to the south, we find a very different picture, for there are several centers where the nature of various metals was discovered and methods of working them were devised. First came the hammering of gold into sheets which could be cut to shape and embossed or joined by the application of heat. This is credited to the Chavin culture in northern Peru. Several centuries later, casting and alloying were invented in two distant regions: in Colombia where the metals were gold and copper, in southern Peru where the metals were copper and tin. Knowledge of these two basic concepts had expanded until they overlapped on the north-central coast of Peru during the Mochica period. A guess date would be ca. A.D. 700. Discovery of platinum and lead came much later, the former in Ecuador, the latter in both Peru and Mexico.

Chavin culture is placed at least as far back as 700 B.C. by radiocarbon dating. Metal objects, however, appeared only after the characteristic style of Chavin stone sculpture had been fully developed. The metal industry was based on hammered gold, mostly in the form of ornaments such as crowns, breastplates (Pl. cvi, cvii), finger rings, pins and - adornments which are foreign to our culture - nose pendants and large ear spools. An important early invention was a method of joining metal sheets which led to the manufacture of hollow beads and figurines. There are a few examples of bimetallic objects, partly of gold and partly of silver (Pl. cxxxii, *right*).

This early Peruvian metal industry never became very productive. At the end of the Chavin period, the use of metals languished in the north and apparently died out completely in southern Peru until, after several centuries, the use of copper and the art of casting were discovered, presumably in the vicinity of Lake Titicaca on the Bolivian border. A rapid expansion of the use of metals followed, with the development of new alloys such as bronze, new techniques such as gilding, and many new types of tools and ornaments. Centuries later, the Incas inherited all the Peruvian metal techniques, and the expansion of their empire carried them to such distant lands as Colombia, Argentina and Chile.

In spite of the fame of the Mexican smiths (Pls. l and lix), there is no evidence that metal was manufactured in that country before the end of the ninth century A.D. During the latter part of the Aztec regime a system of tribute brought a large amount of gold to their capital but archaeological discoveries of metal have been few.

It has been suggested that the entire Peruvian metallurgical system was brought to Mexico by sea as a unit. It is indeed true that the same basic metals - gold, silver, copper, tin and lead - were known in both countries, but the uses to which they were put and the alloys made from them are quite distinct. Also there is the negative evidence that the big Kon Tiki-type sailing rafts with centerboards, necessary for such a voyage, were not invented until a much later period. On the other hand, metal artifacts from southern Central America and even from Colombia have been found in Mexico in fair quantity and their influence on Mexican styles can be demonstrated.

The Maya, gifted artisans and craftsmen, began to acquire metal artifacts by trade at the end of the Classic period. Discovery of a *tumbaga* figure under a dated stela places trade with the Isthmus and the manufacture of *tumbaga* alloys before A.D. 800. The Maya, however, with possible exceptions in the Guatemalan highlands, did not cast any metal, but occasionally they embossed designs of their own choosing on gold plaques which they secured by trade.

PLATES

Top left: Archaic pottery figurines. Mexico. *Cat. Nos. 1–2.—Bottom:* Jadeite carvings. Olmec. Mexico. *Cat. Nos. 3–5.*
Upper right: Jadeite 'stilettos' probably used for blood sacrifice. Olmec. Mexico. *Cat. Nos. 6–7.*

I

Diopside-jadeite figure. Olmec. Mexico. *Cat. No. 8.*

Blue jadeite bust. Olmec. Mexico. *Cat. No. 9.*

Serpentine female figure. Olmec. Mexico. *Cat. No. 10.*

Serpentine male figure. Olmec. Mexico. *Cat. No. 11.*

Top right: Serpentine dancing figure. Olmec. *Cat. No. 12.—Bottom:* Diopside-jadeite head. Olmec. *Cat. No. 13.*
Top left: Tremolite mask. Olmec. Mexico. *Cat. No. 14.*

Marble jaguar mask. Olmec. Mexico. *Cat. No. 15.*

Rock quartz and chalcedony jaguar mask.
Olmec. Mexico. *Cat. No. 16.*

Pottery head. Olmec(?). Mexico.
Cat. No. 16–A.

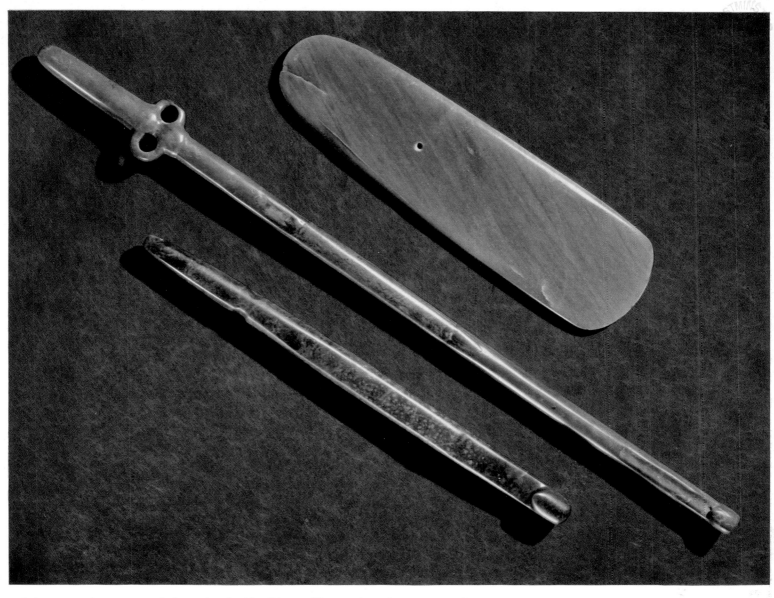

Jadeite spear-throwers and chopping knife. Olmec (?). Mexico. *Cat. Nos. 17-A, 17-B, 17-C.*

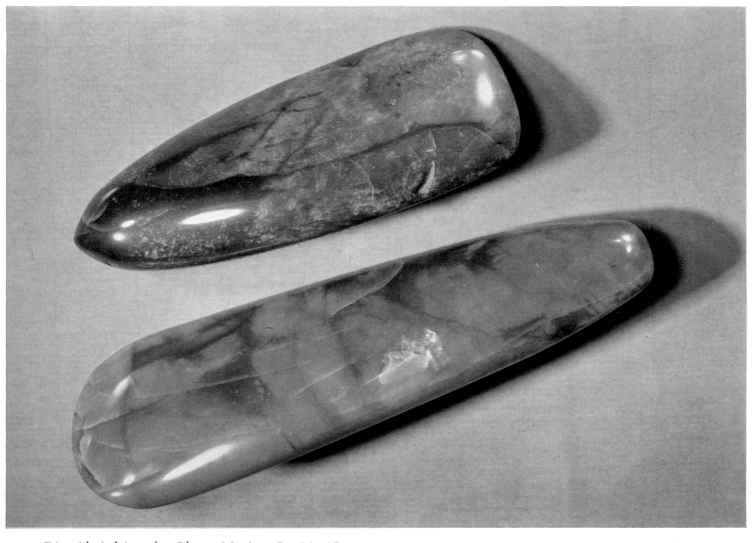

Diopside-jadeite celts. Olmec. Mexico. *Cat. No. 17.*

Center: Porphyry jaguar mask. Olmec. *Cat. No. 18.— Top and right:* Pair of diopside-jadeite tubular beads. Olmec. *Cat. No. 19.*
Bottom: Diopside-jadeite breast-plate. Olmec. Mexico. *Cat. No. 20.*

Slate mirror-back. Early Classic Veracruz. Mexico. *Cat. No. 20-A.*

Diorite porphyry yoke. Classic Veracruz. Mexico. *Cat. No. 21.*

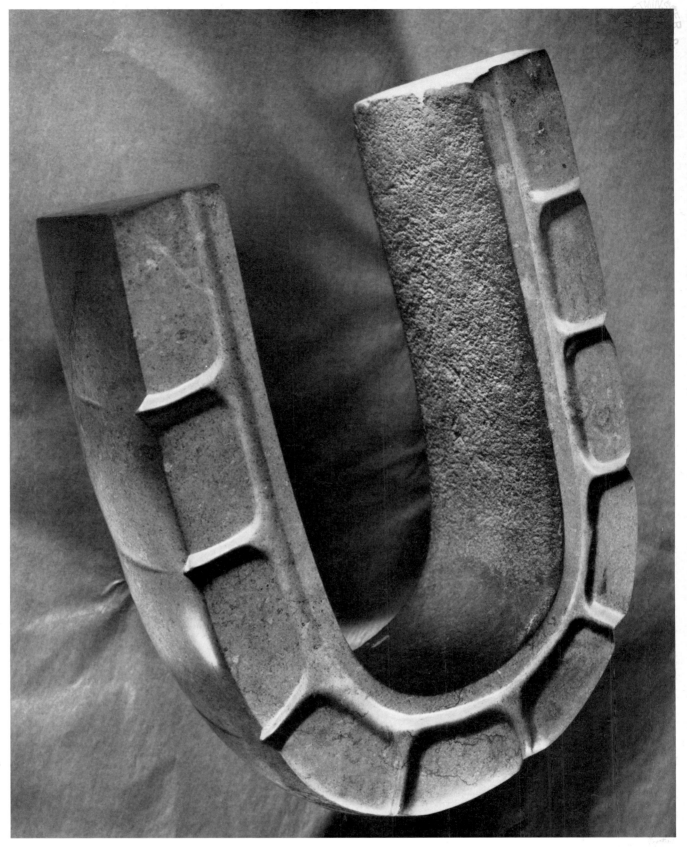

Metadiorite yoke. Classic Veracruz. Mexico. *Cat. No. 22.*

Marble *hacha*. Late Classic Veracruz. Mexico. *Cat. No. 23-A.*

Marble *hacha*. Classic Veracruz. Mexico. *Cat. No. 23.*

Basalt *hacha*. Classic Veracruz. Mexico. *Cat. No. 24.*

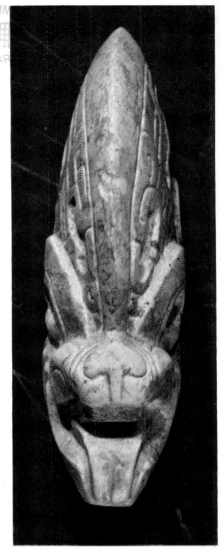

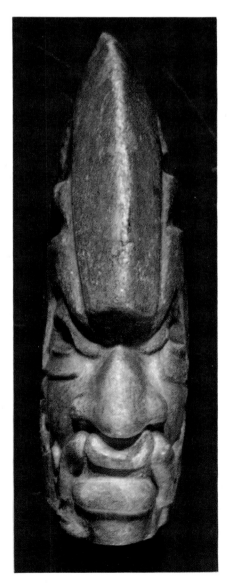

Marble *hachas*. Classic Veracruz. Mexico.— *Top: Cat. No. 25.—Bottom: Cat. No. 26.*

Basalt *hacha*. Classic Veracruz. Mexico. *Cat. No. 27.*

Metadiorite *hacha*. Classic Veracruz. Mexico. *Cat. No. 27-A.*

Basalt head. Classic Veracruz. Mexico. *Cat. No. 28.*

Onyx marble head. Classic Veracruz. Mexico. *Cat. No. 29.*

Marble head. Classic Veracruz. Mexico. *Cat. No. 30.*

Diorite palmate stone. Classic Veracruz. Mexico. *Cat. No. 31.*

Pottery head. Remojadas style. Veracruz. Mexico. *Cat. No. 32.*

Limestone mask. Style of Teotihuacan. Mexico. *Cat. No. 34.*

Green serpentine mask. Style of Teotihuacan. Mexico. *Cat. No. 36.*

Jadeite mask. Style of Teotihuacan. Mexico. *Cat. No. 37.*

Miscellaneous stone carvings. Style of Teotihuacan. Mexico.—*Top: Cat. No. 38.—Center right: Cat. No. 39.*
Center left: Cat. No. 40.—Bottom: Cat. Nos. 43, 41, 42.

Frescoed brown-ware pottery jar.
Style of Teotihuacan. Mexico.
Cat. No. 44.

Frescoed brown-ware pottery jar. Style of Teotihuacan. Mexico. *Cat. No. 45.*

Frescoed brown–ware pottery jar. Style of Teotihuacan. Mexico. *Cat. No. 46.*

Frescoed brown-ware tripod jar. Style of Teotihuacan. Mexico. *Cat. No. 47.*

Frescoed orange-ware tripod jar. Style of Teotihuacan. Mexico. *Cat. No. 48.*

Frescoed orange-ware bowl. Style of Teotihuacan. Mexico. *Cat. No. 49.*

Kneeling figures of Chalchihuitlicue, Aztec goddess of Water. Mexico.—*Left: Cat. No. 51.—Right: Cat. No. 50.*

Stone figure of Tlazolteotl, Aztec goddess
of Childbirth. Mexico. *Cat. No. 52.*

Stone figure of Tlazolteotl, Aztec goddess of Childbirth. Mexico. *Cat. No. 52.*

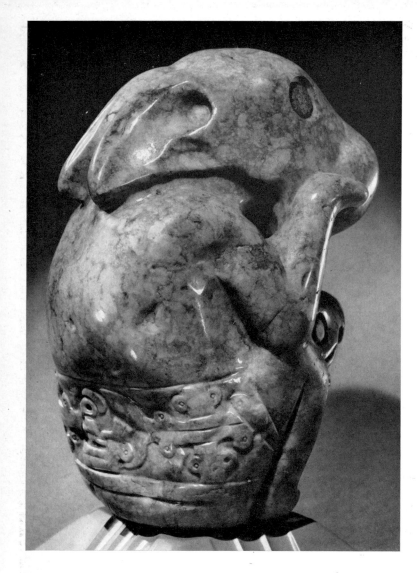

Jadeite figure of a rabbit. Aztec. Mexico. *Cat. No. 53.*

Jadeite figure of a rabbit. Aztec. Mexico. *Cat. No. 53.*

Porphyry coiled rattlesnake. Aztec. Mexico. *Cat. No. 54.*

Base of rattlesnake seen in Plate XL.

Black basalt feathered serpent. Aztec. Mexico. *Cat. No. 55.*

Ceremonial serpent of quartz-diorite. Aztec. Mexico. *Cat. No. 56.*

Aztec mask. Mexico. *Cat. No. 57.*

Figure of the Aztec god Xipe dressed in a flayed human skin, seen from the back. Mexico. *Cat. No. 58.*

Figure of the Aztec god Xipe dressed in a flayed human skin. Mexico. *Cat. No. 58.*

Shell head of the god Xipe. *Cat. No. 59.* — Shell necklace representing skulls. Aztec. Mexico. *Cat. No. 60.*

Obsidian skull. Aztec. Mexico. *Cat. No. 61.*

Top: Crystal skull. Aztec. *Cat. No. 62.* — *Bottom right:* Jadeite skull. Aztec. *Cat. No. 63.* — *Bottom left:* Jadeite cup. Aztec. Mexico. *Cat. No. 64.* — Necklace of stone beads. Mexico. *Cat. No. 78.*

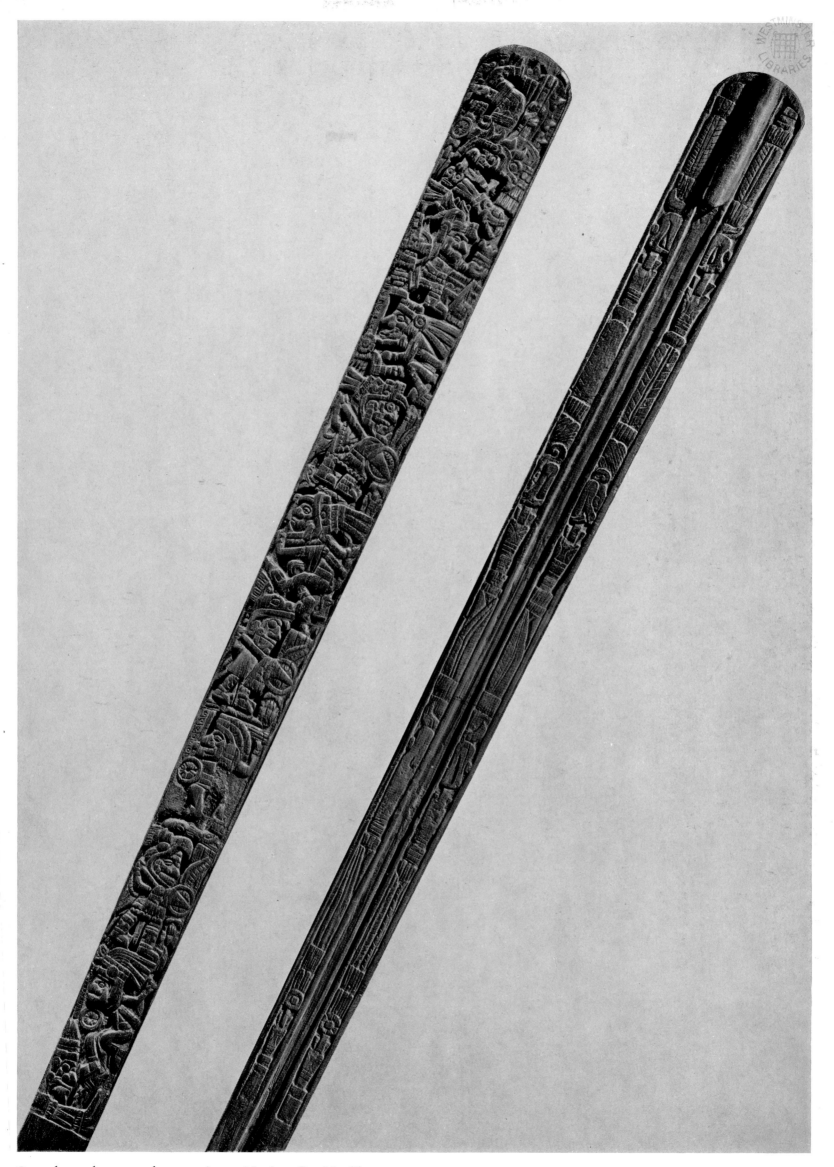

Carved wooden spear-thrower. Aztec. Mexico. *Cat. No. 65.*

Aztec ear-spools and labrets. Mexico. *Top: Cat. Nos. 70, 69, 68.—Second row: Cat. Nos. 66, 69, 67.—Third row: Cat. No. 71. Bottom left and right: Cat. No. 72.—Bottom center: Cat. No. 73.*

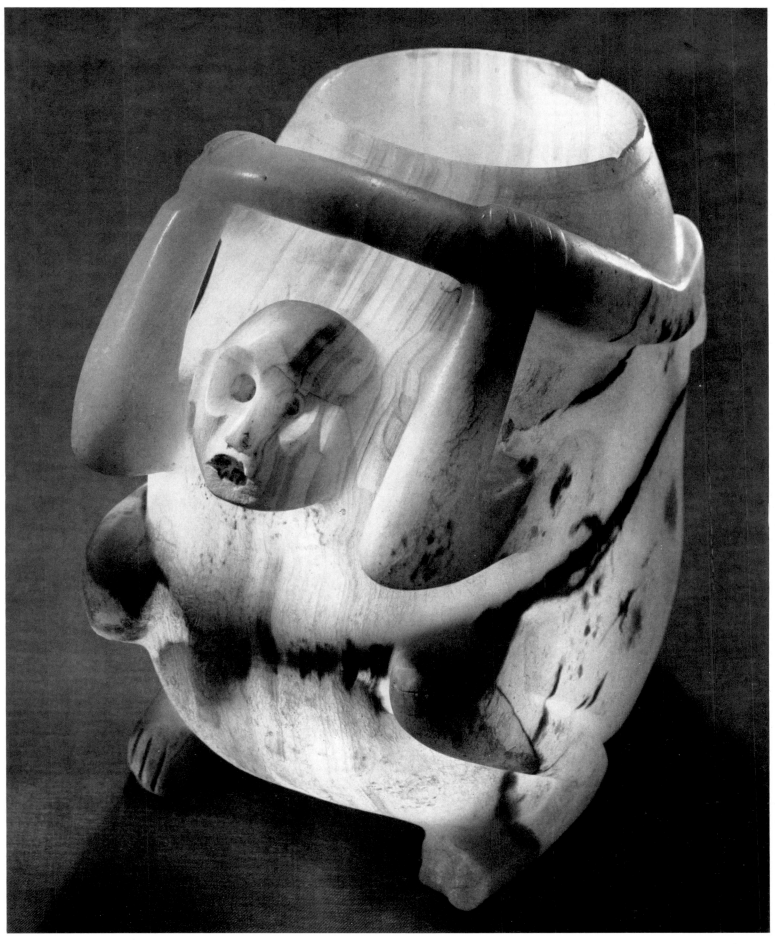

Onyx marble effigy jar. Mexico. *Cat. No. 74.*

Flaring onyx marble jar. Veracruz. Mexico. *Cat. No. 75.*

Onyx marble jar. Mexico. *Cat. No. 76.*

Globular onyx marble jar. Mexico. *Cat. No. 77.*

Winged pendant of diopside-jadeite. Mexico. *Cat. No. 81.*

Top left: Stone head. Mexico. *Cat. No. 85.—Left center:* Stone head. Mexico. *Cat. No. 83.*
Center: Jadeite bar pendant. Mexico. *Cat. No. 79.—Bottom right:* Stone head. Mexico. *Cat. No. 84.*

Top: Diopside-jadeite head. Mexico. *Cat. No. 87.* —*Bottom:* Bar pendant. Mexico. *Cat. No. 80.*

Top: Marble head. Mexico. *Cat. No. 86.—Bottom:* Pair of quartzite ear disks. Mexico. *Cat. No. 82.*

Porphyry head and jadeite disks and plaque. Mexico.— *Top: Cat. Nos. 90, 89.— Bottom: Cat. Nos. 91, 88.*

Top: Two jadeite plaques. Zapotec style (?). Mexico. *Cat. Nos. 93, 95.—Bottom left:* Prehnite pendant. Zapotec style (?). Mexico. *Cat. No. 94.—Bottom center:* Two grooved diopside-jadeite beads. Mexico. *Cat. No. 92.—Bottom right:* Seated diopside-jadeite figure. Mixtec style. Mexico. *Cat. No. 96.*

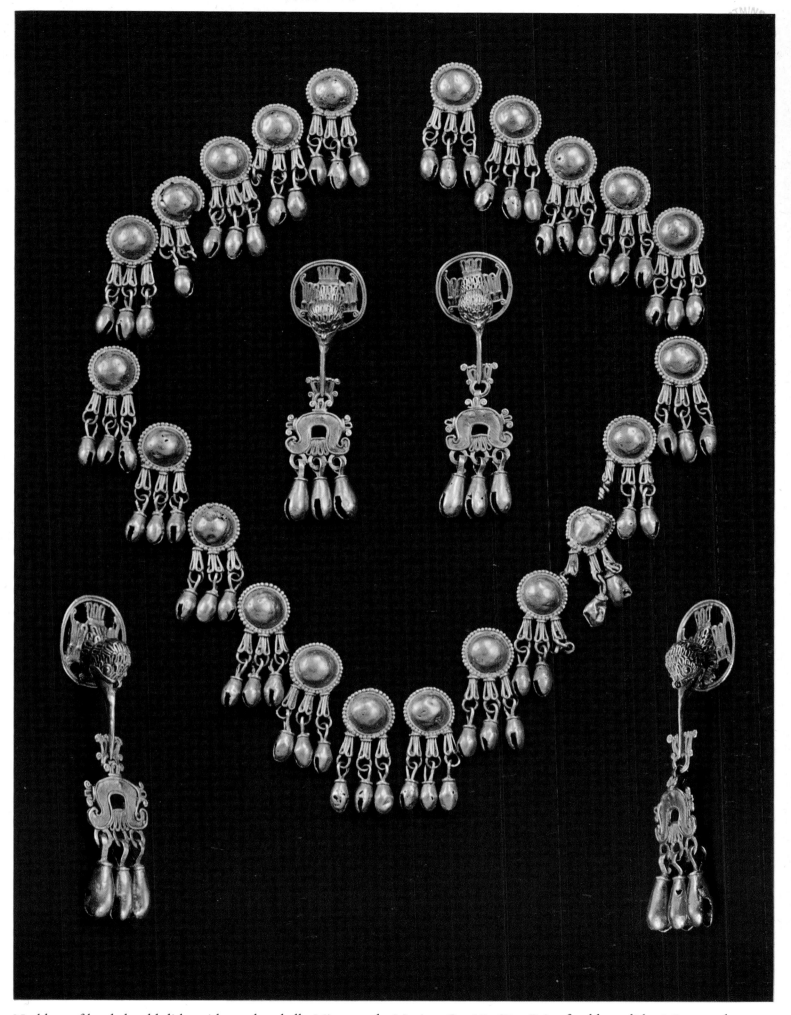

Necklace of beaded gold disks with pendant bells. Mixtec style. Mexico. *Cat. No. 97.* — Pair of gold ear disks. Mixtec style. Mexico. *Cat. No. 98.*

Wooden mask covered with mosaic of turquoise, mother-of-pearl and pink shell. Mixtec culture. Mexico. *Cat. No. 99.*

Sericite jaguar. Mexico. *Cat. No. 100.*

Effigy jar representing a hunter carrying a deer. Tarascan style. Mexico. *Cat. No. 101.*

Stone head of the Maize god.
Classic Maya. Copan, Honduras.
Cat. No. 102.

Painted stucco head. Classic Maya.
Mexico. *Cat. No. 103.*

Two jadeite pendants. Late Classic Maya. Guatemala. *Cat. Nos. 104-B, 104-A.*

Pair of carved shell plaques with jade inlays. Late Classic Maya. Mexico. *Cat. No. 104.*

Maya jadeite ornaments. Mexico.— *Top: Cat. Nos. 105, 106, 107.— Second row: Cat. Nos. 109, 108, 110.*
Third row: Cat. Nos. 111, 112, 115.— Bottom: Cat. Nos. 113, 114, 116.

Top: Muscovite mask. Mexico. *Cat. No. 116-A.*—Pair of ear disks. Late Classic Maya. Guatemala. *Cat. No. 116-B.*
Bottom: Set of fifty-eight small ear-disks. Late Classic Maya. Guatemala. *Cat. No. 116-C.*

Miscellaneous jadeite artifacts. Late Classic Maya. Guatemala. *Top left: Cat. No. 116–G.—Second left: Cat. No. 116–J.— Top center: Cat. No. 116–H.—Second, left center: Cat. No. 116–K.—Third left center: Cat. No. 116–N.—Fourth, left center: Cat. 116–E.— Top right: Cat. No. 116–F.—Second right: Cat. No. 116–I. — Third, right center: Cat. No. 116–L.—Fourth, right center: Cat. No. 116–D.—Fifth, right center: Cat. No. 116–O. —Sixth, right center: Cat. No. 116–P.—Seventh, right center: Cat. No. 116–Q.—Necklace: Cat. No. 116–M.*

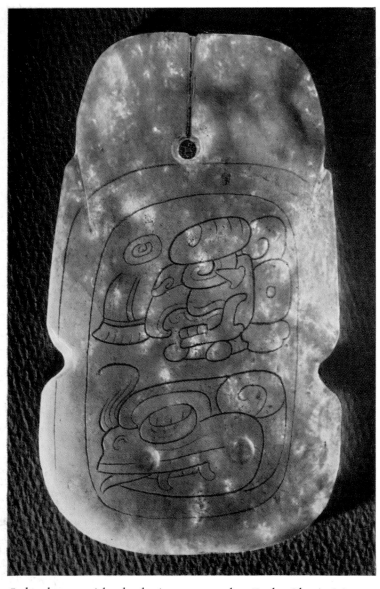

Jade plaque with glyphs in a cartouche. Early Classic Maya. Mexico. *Cat. No. 117.*

Jadeite plaque carved in relief. Late Classic Maya. Guatemala. *Cat. No. 118.*

Pottery statuette of a man. Classic Maya. Jaina style. Mexico. *Cat. No. 119.*

Pottery statuette of a man. Classic Maya. Jaina style. Mexico. *Cat. No. 120.*

Pottery figurines of a warrior and a seated woman. Late Classic Maya. Jaina and Jonuta styles. Mexico. *Cat. Nos. 121–122.*

Pottery figurines of a man and a woman. Late Classic Maya. Jaina style. Mexico. *Cat. Nos. 123–124.*

Pottery figurine of a man. Late Classic Maya.
Jaina style. Mexico. *Cat. No. 125.*

Pottery figurine-whistle. Classic Maya. Jaina style. Mexico. *Cat. No. 126.*

Pottery figurine of an old man embracing a young girl. Classic Maya. Jaina style. Mexico. *Cat. No. 127.*

Details of pottery figurine-whistle. Late Classic Maya. Style of Jonuta?
Mexico. *Cat. No. 131.*

Pottery figurine-whistle. Late Classic Maya. Style of Jonuta? Mexico. *Cat. No. 131.*

Pottery figurines. Classic Maya. Jaina style. Mexico. *Cat. Nos. 129, 128, 130.*

Polychrome pottery bowl. Late Classic Maya. Mexico. *Cat. No. 132.*

Polychrome jar. Late Classic Maya. Mexico. *Cat. No. 135.*

Polychrome jar. Late Classic Maya. Mexico. *Cat. No. 134.*

Extended design from the jar in Plate LXXX (*Cat. No. 135*). (From a water-colour by M. Louise Baker.)

Polychrome jar. Classic Maya. Mexico. *Cat. No. 133.*

Slate-ware jar. Late Classic Maya. Yucatan, Mexico. *Cat. No. 139.*

Polished orange-ware bowl. Tula-Toltec period. Yucatan, Mexico. *Cat. No. 136.*

Carved slate-ware bowl. Late Classic Maya. Yucatan, Mexico. *Cat. No. 137.*

LXXXIII

Carved slate-ware bowl. Late Classic Maya. Yucatan, Mexico. *Cat. No. 137.*

Light-brown clay bowl. Classic Maya. Yucatan, Mexico. *Cat. No. 138.*

Onyx marble bowl. Classic Maya. Campeche, Mexico. *Cat. No. 140.*

Onyx marble bowl. Classic Maya. Campeche, Mexico. *Cat. No. 140.*

Marble bowl. Style of Ulua Valley, Honduras. Found in Costa Rica. *Cat. No. 142.*

Onyx marble bowl. Classic Maya. Campeche, Mexico. *Cat. No. 141.*

Jade ornaments. Nicoya peninsula, Costa Rica. Necklace, *Cat. No. 145.* — *Top: Cat. No. 179.* — *Center row: Cat. Nos. 149, 154, 160.*
Below No. 154: Cat. Nos. 166, 169. — *Bottom: Cat. Nos. 180, 181.*

Diorite club head. *Cat. No. 143.* — Jadeite necklace. *Cat. No. 144.* Nicoya peninsula, Costa Rica.

Jadeite ornaments. Nicoya peninsula, Costa Rica.— *Top: Cat. Nos. 177, 178.*—*Center: Cat. No. 182.*—*Bottom: Cat. Nos. 146, 147, 148.*

Jadeite ornaments. Guápiles, Costa Rica.—*Left: Cat. Nos. 188, 189.*— *Top right: Cat. No. 187.*—*Bottom: Cat. Nos. 190, 191, 192, 193.*

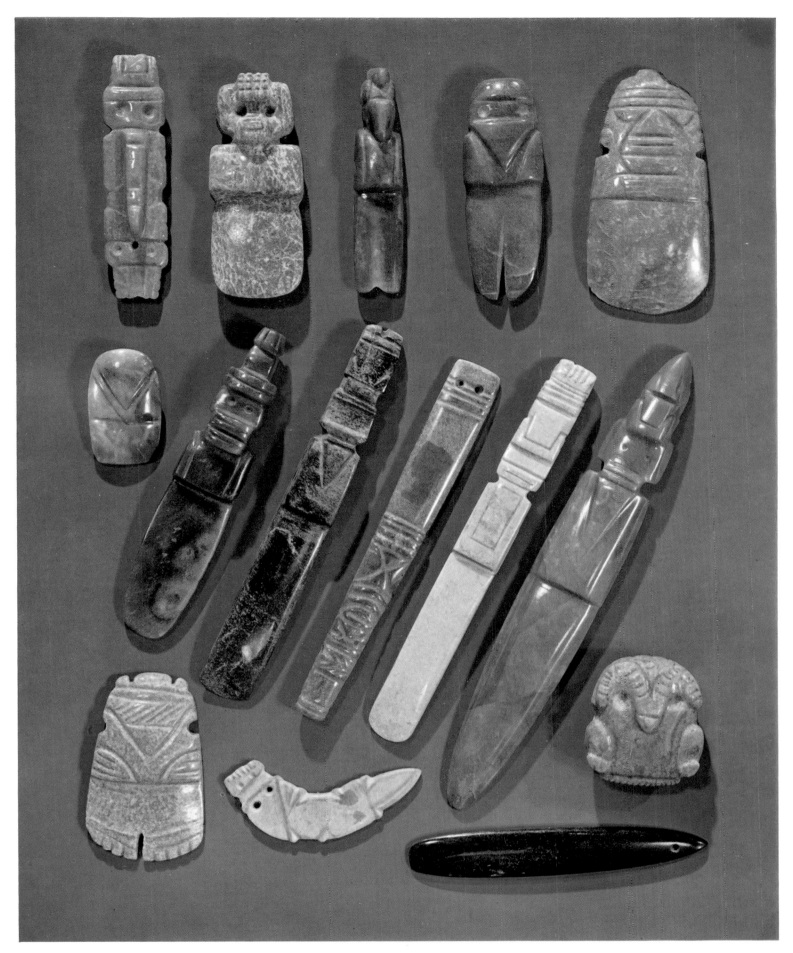

Jadeite ornaments. Nicoya peninsula, Costa Rica.—*Top row: Cat. Nos. 170, 161, 155, 156, 150.—Second row: Cat. Nos. 167, 162, 163, 172, 164, 151, 168.—Bottom: Cat. Nos. 152, 171, 183.*

Jadeite ornaments. Nicoya peninsula, Costa Rica.—*Top row: Cat. Nos. 157, 174, 165, 184.—Center: Cat. Nos. 185, 186, 175, 176.*
Bottom row: Cat. Nos. 158, 153, 173, 159.

Jadeite ornaments. Guápiles, Costa Rica.—*Top row: Cat. Nos. 201, 197, 198.—Below No. 197: Cat. No. 200. Center row: Cat. Nos. 202, 203, 194.—Bottom row: Cat. Nos. 196, 195, 199.*

Jadeite pendants. Guápiles, Costa Rica.—*Top: Cat. No. 208.—Center: Cat. Nos. 204, 205.*
Bottom: Cat. Nos. 206, 207.

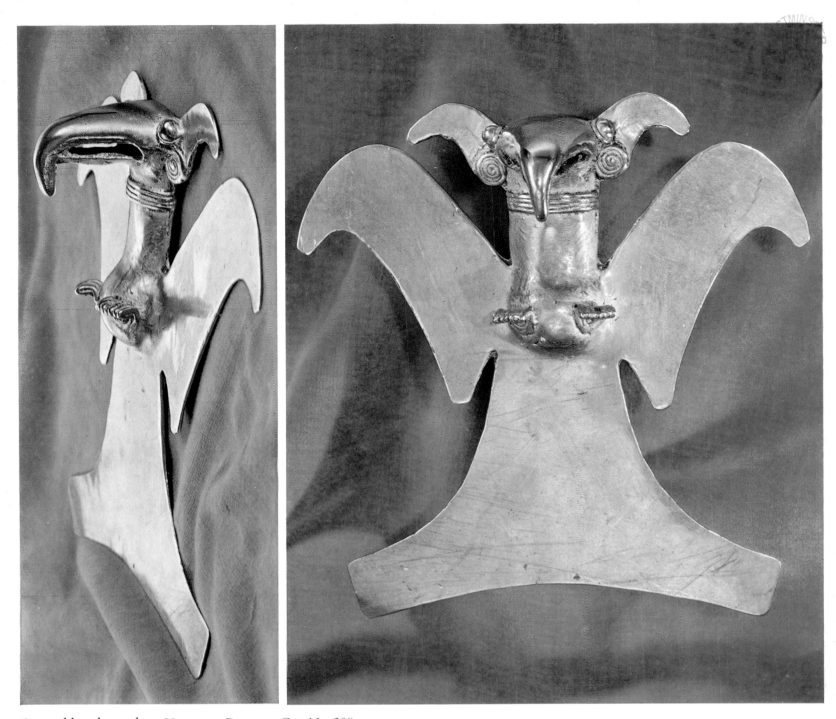

Cast gold eagle pendant. Veraguas, Panama. *Cat. No. 209.*

Cast gold and tumbaga eagle pendants. Veraguas, Panama.—*Top: Cat. No. 210.*—*Bottom: Cat. Nos. 211, 212.*

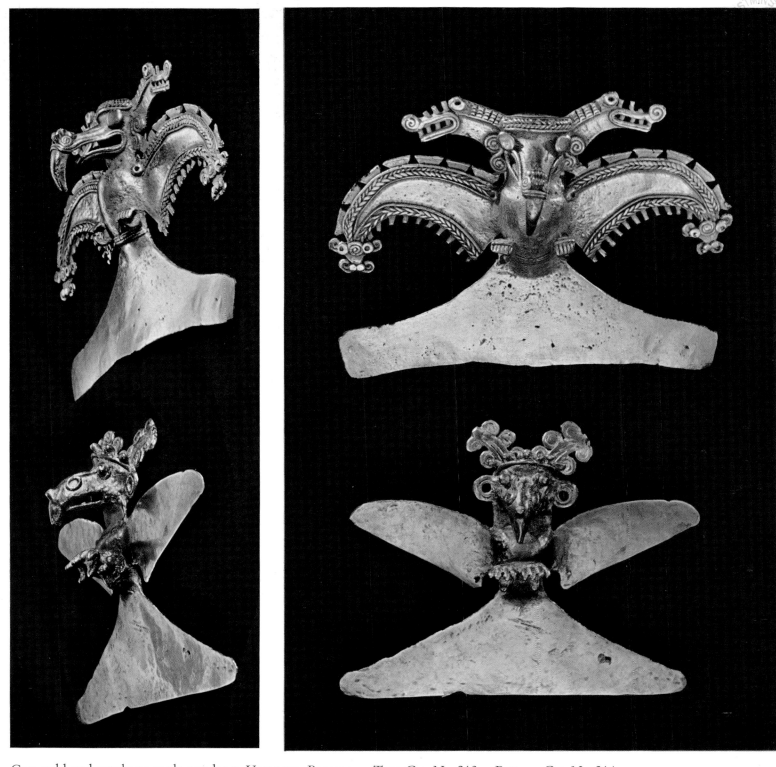

Cast gold and tumbaga eagle pendants. Veraguas, Panama.—*Top: Cat. No. 213.*—*Bottom: Cat. No. 214.*

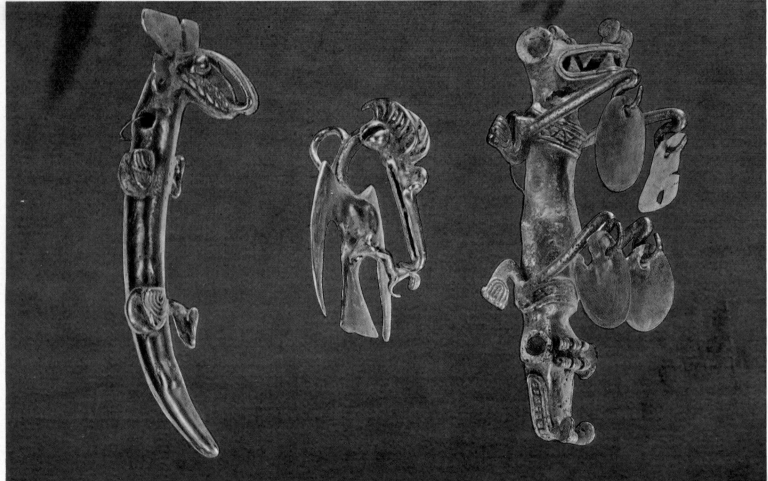

Cast gold pendants. Veraguas, Panama. *Cat. Nos. 228, 219, 226.*

C

Cast gold pendants, representing monkeys and men. Veraguas, Panama.—*Top: Cat. Nos. 229, 230, 231.—Bottom: Cat. Nos. 235, 232, 236.*

Cast gold pendants. Veraguas, Panama.— *Top row: Cat. Nos. 239, 241, 240.— Second row: Cat. Nos. 216, 215, 233.— Bottom row: Cat. Nos. 217, 218, 242.*

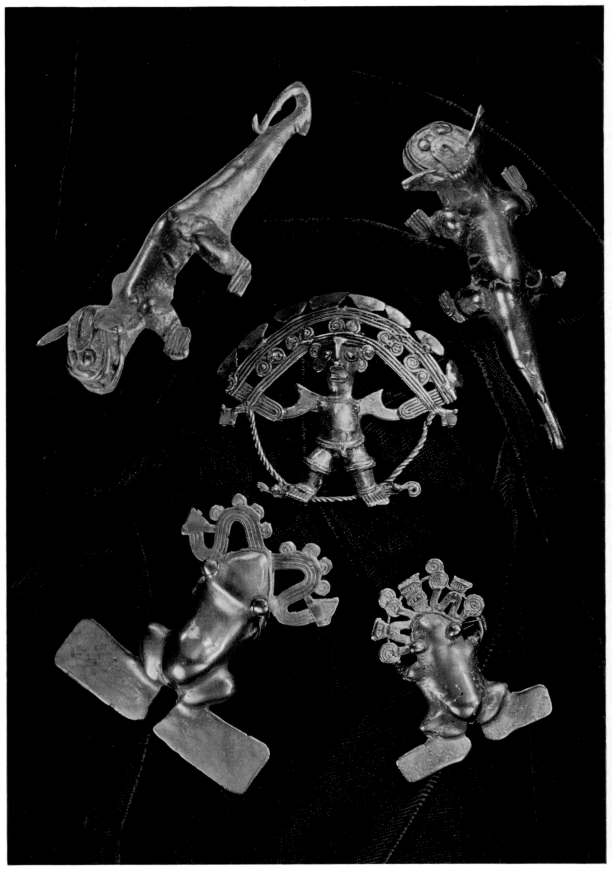

Cast gold pendants. Veraguas, Panama.—*Top left and right: Cat. No. 223.—Center: Cat. No. 234.*
Bottom left: Cat. No. 220.—Bottom right: Cat. No. 221.

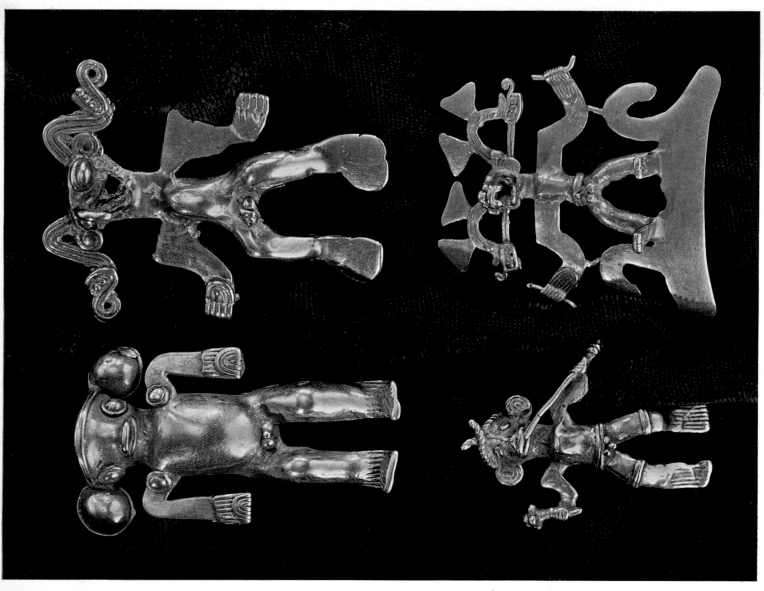

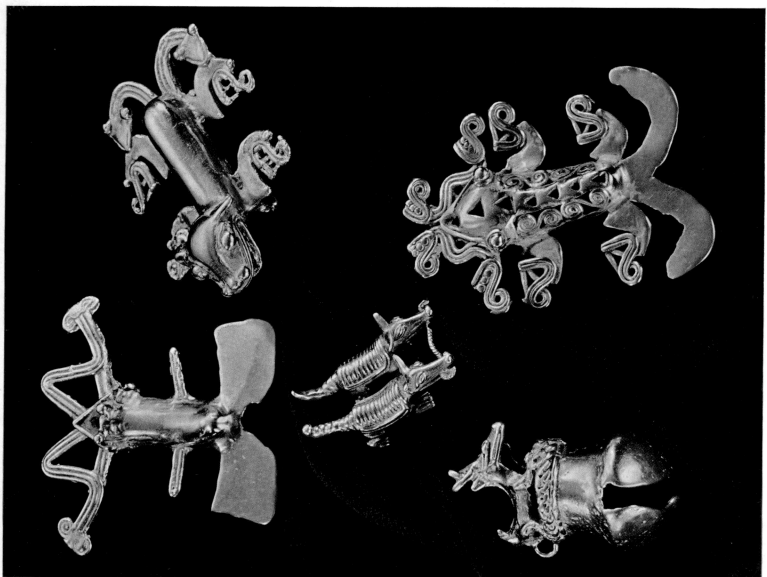

Cast gold pendants. Veraguas, Panama. — Top: Cat. Nos. 222, 224, 237, 243. — Below No. 222: Cat. No. 227. — Bottom: Cat. Nos. 245, 225, 238, 244.

Cast gold bells. Veraguas, Panama.— *Top: Cat. Nos. 250, 248.— Center: Cat. No. 249.— Bottom: Cat. Nos. 247, 246.*

Hammered gold disks. Veraguas, Panama. — *Top: Cat. Nos. 251, 252.* — *Bottom: Cat. Nos. 253, 254.*

Hammered gold disks. Veraguas, Panama. — *Left: Cat. No. 255.* — *Top right: Cat. No. 256.* — *Bottom right: Cat. Nos. 258, 257.*

CVII

Hammered gold disk and cast gold pendants. Coclé style, Panama.—*Left: Cat. No. 263.* Venado Beach.—*Top right: Cat. No. 260.*
Bottom right: Cat. No. 261.

Top: Agate pendant. *Cat. No. 273.*—*Bottom:* Beaten gold plaque. *Cat. No. 262.* Sitio Conte, Coclé, Panama.

Cast gold pendants and shell nose ornament. Venado Beach, Panama.—*At corners: Cat. No. 266.—Top center: Cat. Nos. 264, 265. Bottom center: Cat. No. 269.*

Top left and right: Cast gold pendants. Colombia. *Cat. Nos. 283, 284.* — *Center:* Necklace of gold birds and necklace of gold beads. Colombia. *Cat. Nos. 274, 282.* — *Center right and bottom:* Cast gold beads in the form of frogs, double frogs, armadillo and human head. Veraguas, Panama. Scales, × 1¼, × ca. 5. *Cat. No. 259.*

CXI

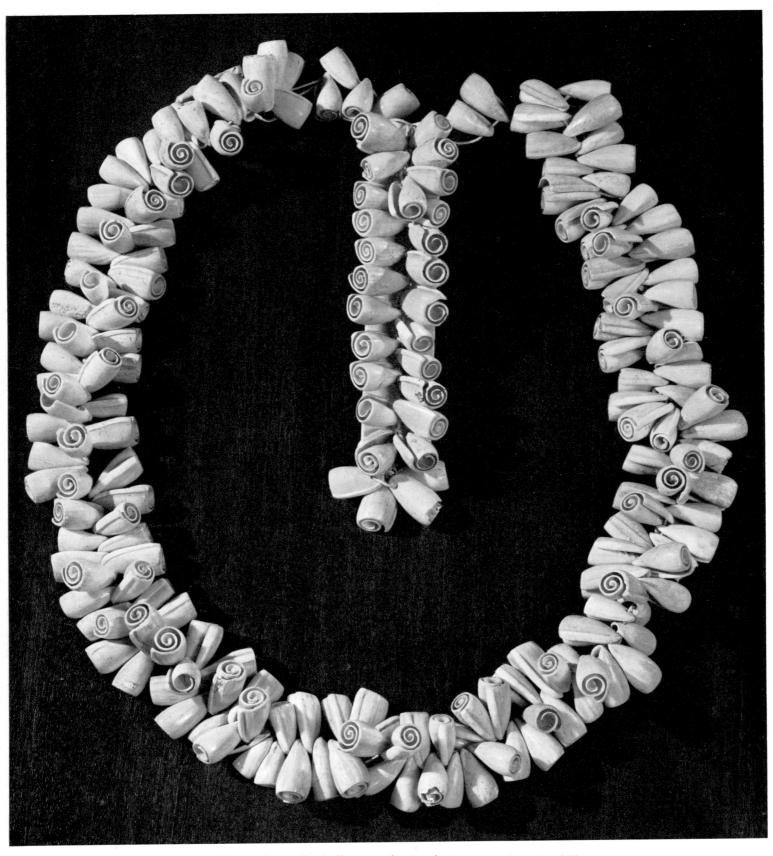

Necklace of olivella shells. Venado Beach, Panama. *Cat. No. 271.*

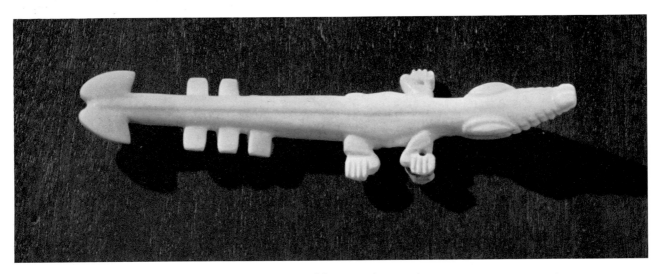

Shell pendant representing a crocodile. Venado Beach, Panama. *Cat. No. 270.*

Gorget of conch shells. Venado Beach, Panama. *Cat. No. 272.*

Shell pendants representing a frog and a bird. Venado Beach, Panama. *Cat. Nos. 268, 267.*

Cast gold objects. Colombia.— *Top left: Cat. Nos. 275, 276.— Top right: Cat. No. 280.— Center: Cat. Nos. 277, 278.*
Bottom: Cat. Nos. 279, 281.

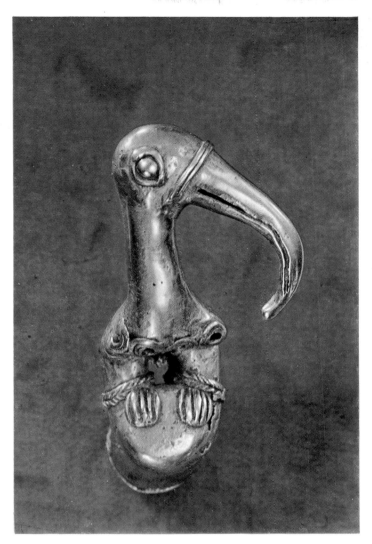
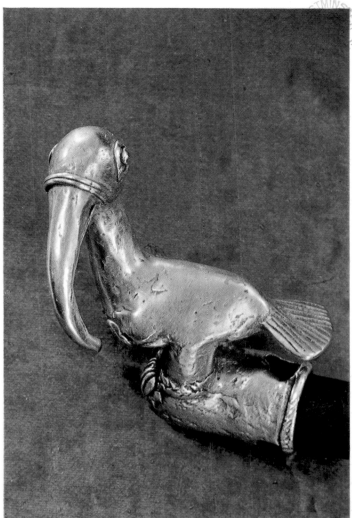

Cast gold bird. Colombia. *Cat. No. 285.*

Cast gold bird. Colombia. *Cat. No. 286.*

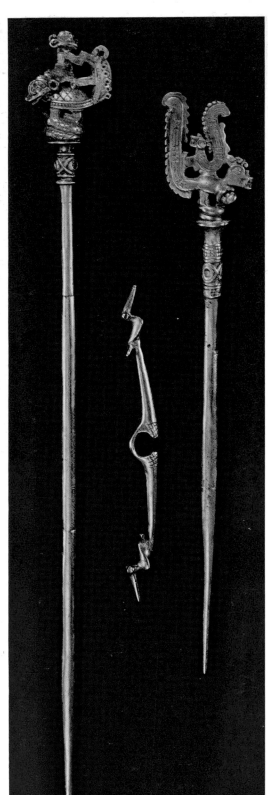

Left: Cast gold pin. *Cat. No. 288.*

Center: Cast gold nose pendant. *Cat. No. 289.*

Right: Cast gold pin. *Cat. No. 287.* Colombia.

Cast gold pendants. Colombia.— *Top left: Cat. No. 294.— Top right: Cat. No. 292.—Center: Cat. No. 291.*
Bottom left: Cat. No. 293.— Bottom right: Cat. No. 290.

Breast plate of hammered sheet gold. Colima style, Colombia. *Cat. No. 295.*

Massive tumbaga pendant representing an anthropomorphic Alligator god. Venezuela. *Cat. No. 296.*

Soapstone cups. North coast of Peru.—*Top: Cat. No. 297.*—*Bottom: Cat. No. 298.*

Extended design from the soapstone cup in Pl. CXX, *top*.

Diorite club head. North coast of Peru. *Cat. No. 299.*

Top left: Hammered gold plaque. Mochica style. *Cat. No. 303.* — *Top right:* Gold spoon. Chavin style. *Cat. No. 300.* — *Bottom left and right:* Inlaid bone handle. Mochica style. *Cat. No. 304.* — *Bottom center:* Gold disk. Chavin style. *Cat. No. 301.* Peru.

Beaten gold disk and fourteen small heads of hammered gold. Peru. *Cat. Nos. 302, 305.*

Pair of sheet gold objects, perhaps dance wands. Peru. *Cat. No. 307.*

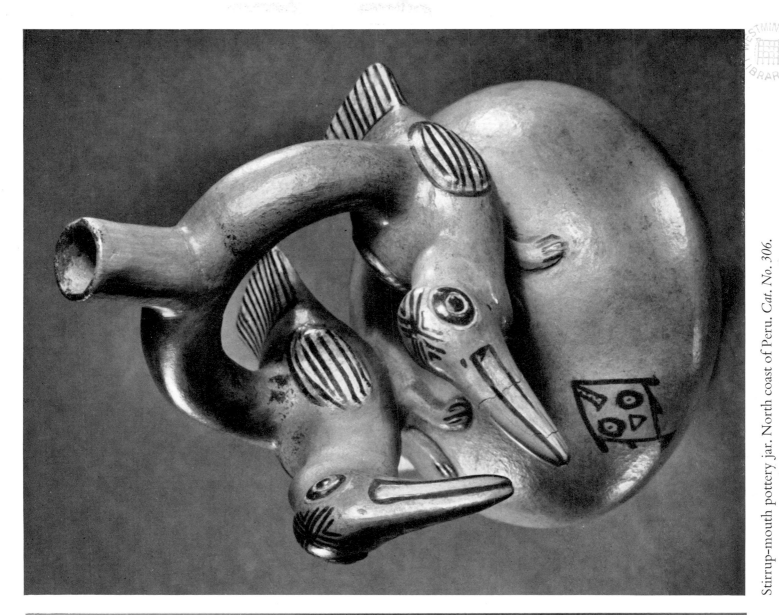

Stirrup-mouth pottery jar. North coast of Peru. *Cat. No. 306.*

Pottery jar representing a skull. South coast of Peru. *Cat. No. 309.*

CXXV

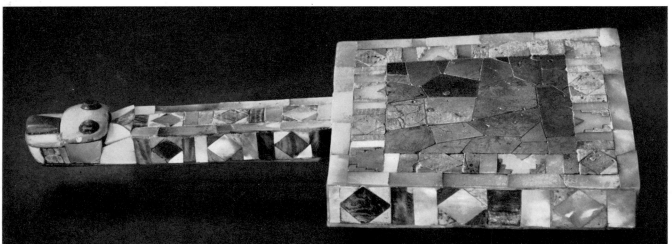

Mosaic mirror of pyrites, turquoise and shell. Coast of Peru. *Cat. No. 310.*

Mosaic mirror of pyrites, turquoise and shell. Coast of Peru. *Cat. No. 310.*

Gold mummy mask. Huarmey, Peru. *Cat. No. 311.*

Gold breast plate. Huarmey, Peru. *Cat. No. 312.*

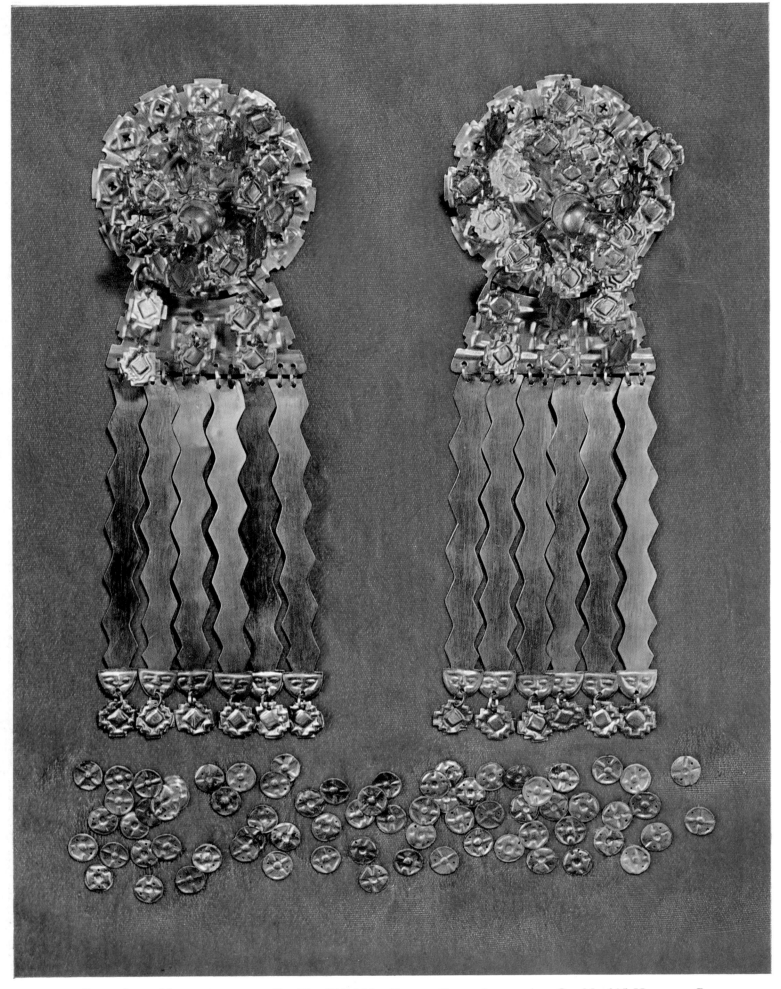

Top: Pair of complex gold ear ornaments. *Cat. Nos. 313–314.*—*Bottom:* Sixty-nine sequins. *Cat. No. 315.* Huarmey, Peru.

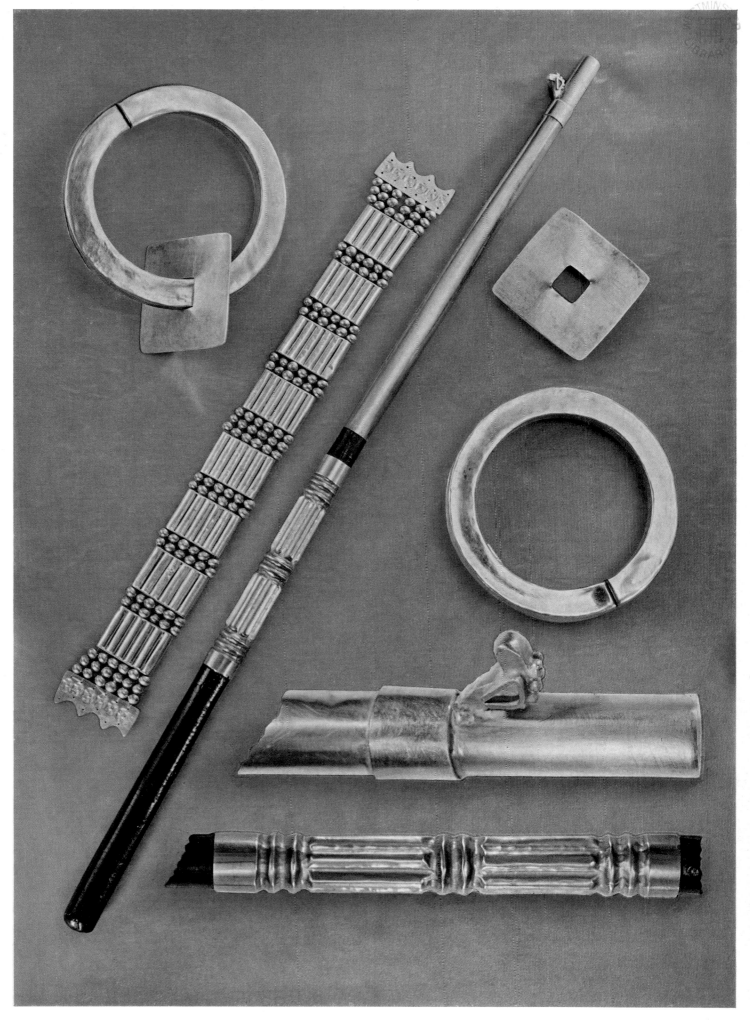

Top right and left: Pair of gold bangles. *Cat. No. 317.—Center left:* Headband of gold beads and tubes. *Cat. No. 316.*
Center: Wooden spear-thrower with gold sheathing. (*Bottom right:* details.) *Cat. No. 319.* Huarmey, Peru.

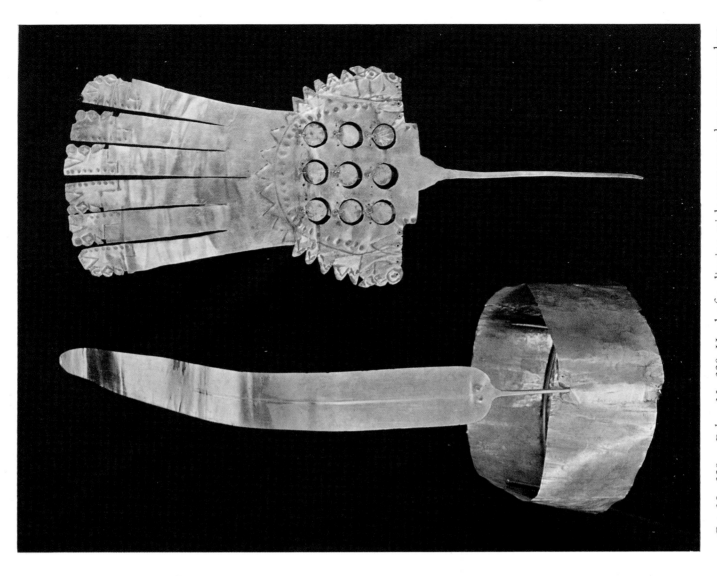

Miscellaneous gold objects. Peru. *Top left:* Pin head. *Cat. No. 325. — Top right:* Stopper for lime case. *Cat. No. 320. — Below No. 320:* Head of a digging stick, wax smoother, nose pendant. *Cat. Nos. 321, 322, 318. — Bottom left and center:* Gold cups. *Cat. Nos. 326 and 327. — Right:* Gold headband and pin. *Cat. No. 323. —* Gold and silver pin. *Cat. No. 324.* Coast of Peru.

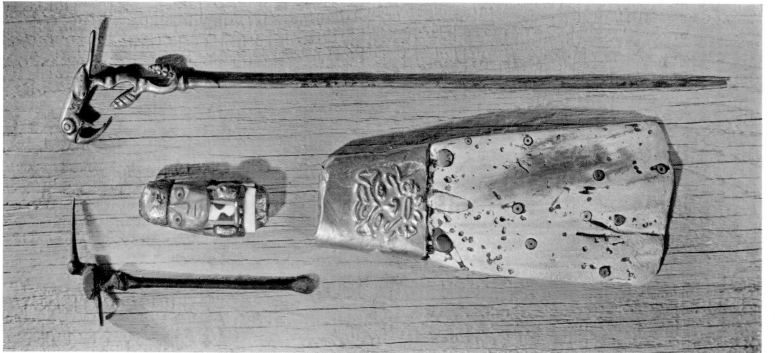

A. *Left:* Ear spoon with bird. *Cat. No. 336.* — *Right:* Silver pin with parrot. *Cat. No. 335.* — *Center top:* Figurine with gold and shell inlays. *Cat. No. 337.* *Center bottom:* Pendant of inlaid shell set in gold. *Cat. No. 308.* Coast of Peru. — B. Details of *Cat. Nos. 336, 337, 335.*

Top: Hollow silver birds. *Cat. No. 329.* — *Center:* Inlaid shell pendant. *Cat. No. 332.* — *Bottom:* Massive gold vessel. *Cat. No. 328.*
Coast of Peru.

Hollow silver figurine. Inca culture, Peru. *Cat. No. 338.*

Top: Mace head in form of a bronze bird inlaid with copper and silver. *Cat. No. 339.* — *Bottom:* Gorget of gold and silver. *Cat. No. 340.* Peru.

Bronze chopping knife inlaid with silver and copper. Peru. *Cat. No. 341.*

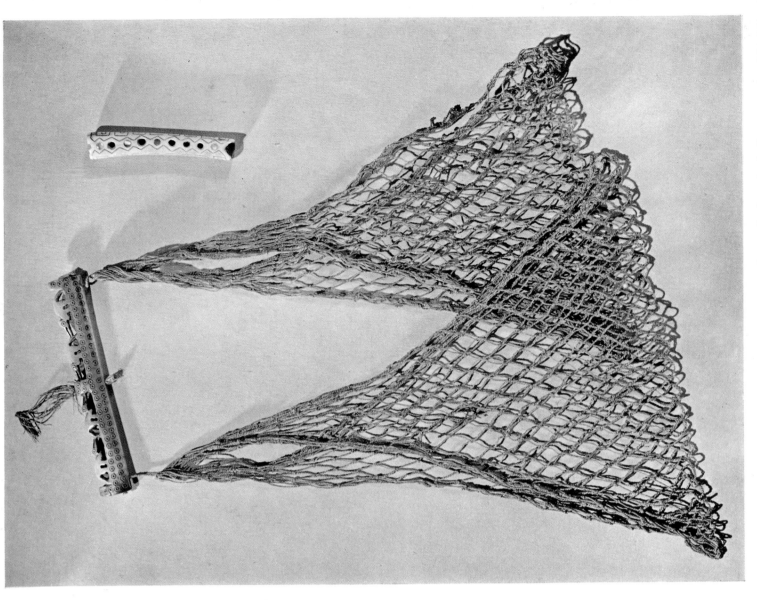

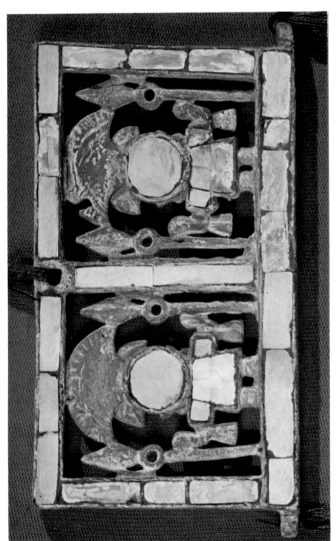

Left: Copper beam for balance scale inlaid with shell. Peru. Cat. No. 334.— Center: Balance–beam scales. Peru. Cat. No. 333.— Top right: Bone flute inlaid with shell. Peru. Cat. No. 331.

Two plaques of silver alloy with symbolic designs. North coast of Peru. *Cat. No. 330.*

Painted cloth made for burial. South coast of Peru. *Cat. No. 342.*

Fragment of an embroidered mantle border.
South coast of Peru. *Cat. No. 343.*

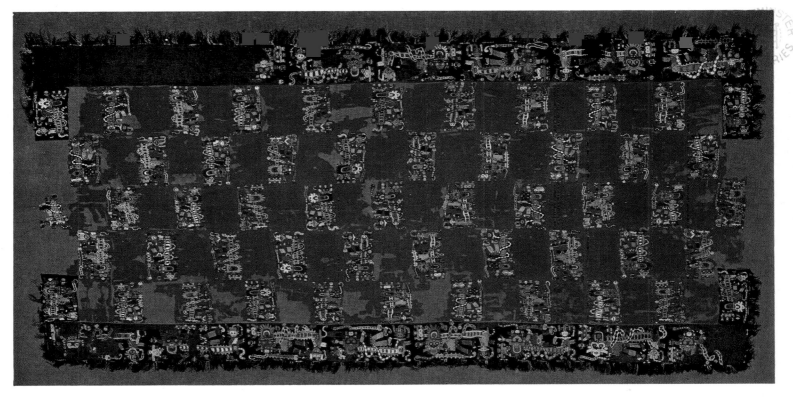

Embroidered mantle. South coast of Peru. *Cat. No. 344.*

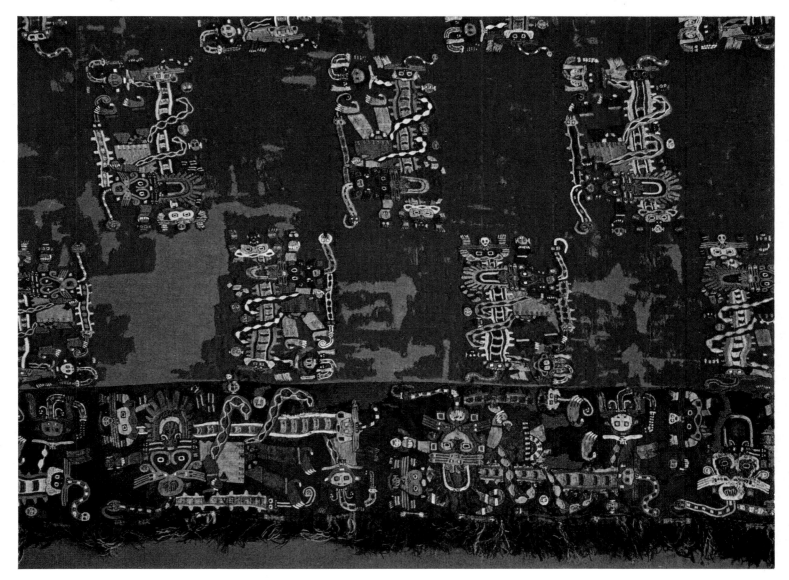

Detail of *Cat. No. 344.*

Tassel for turban of belt-strap. South coast of Peru. *Cat. No. 345.*

Fragment of tapestry. South coast of Peru. *Cat. No. 347.*

Poncho shirt (?). South coast of Peru. *Cat. No. 348.*

Major portion of poncho shirt. Coast of Peru. *Cat. No. 349.*

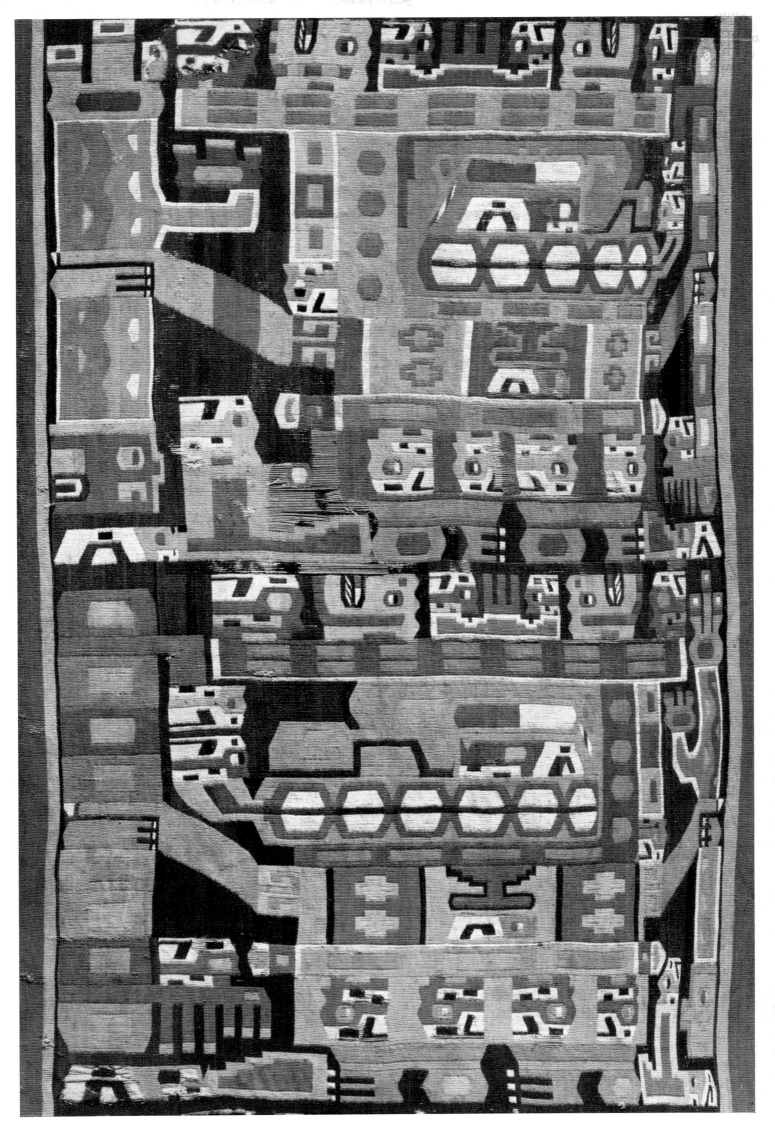

Portion of poncho shirt. Detail from plate CXLIV.

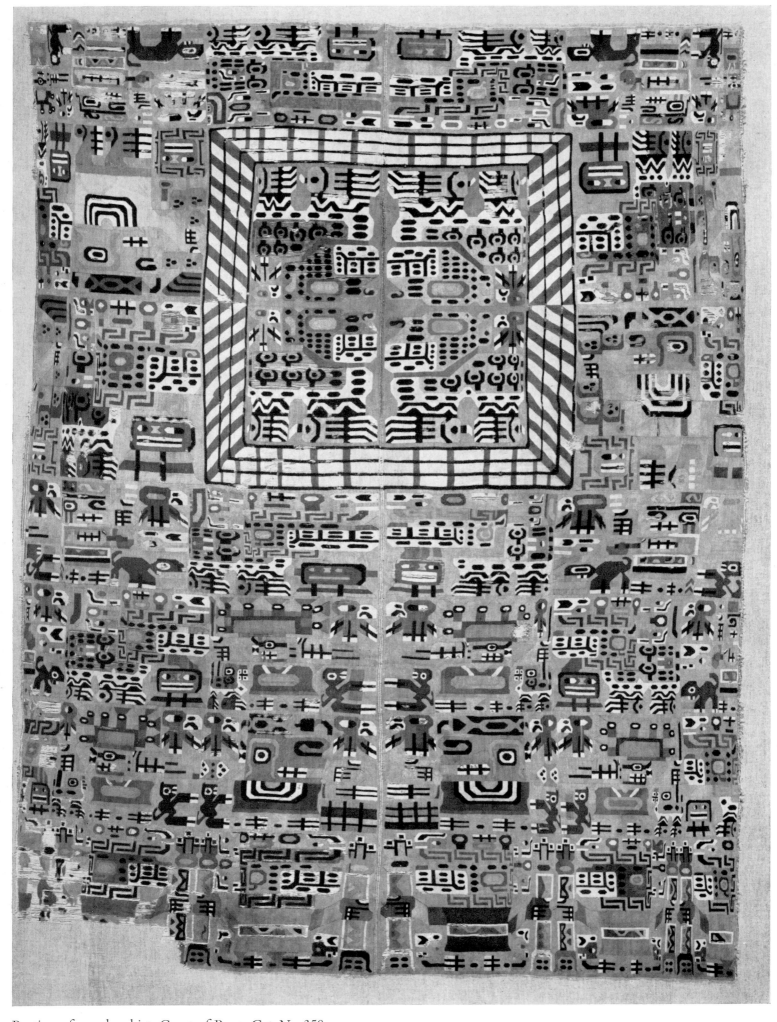

Portion of poncho shirt. Coast of Peru. *Cat. No. 350.*

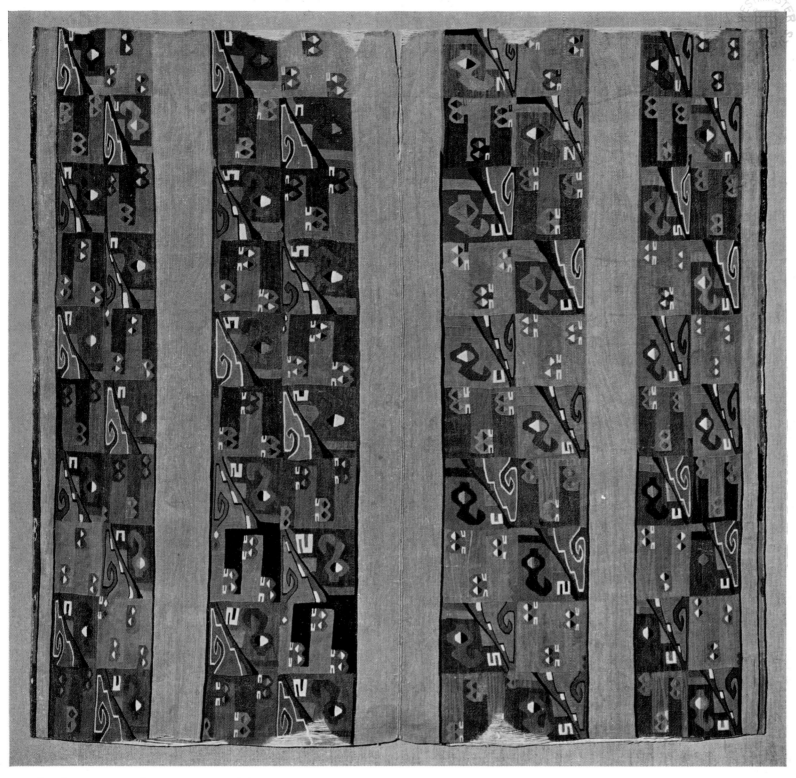

Poncho shirt. Coast of Peru. *Cat. No. 351.*

Fragment of poncho shirt or tunic. Coast of Peru. *Cat. No. 352.*

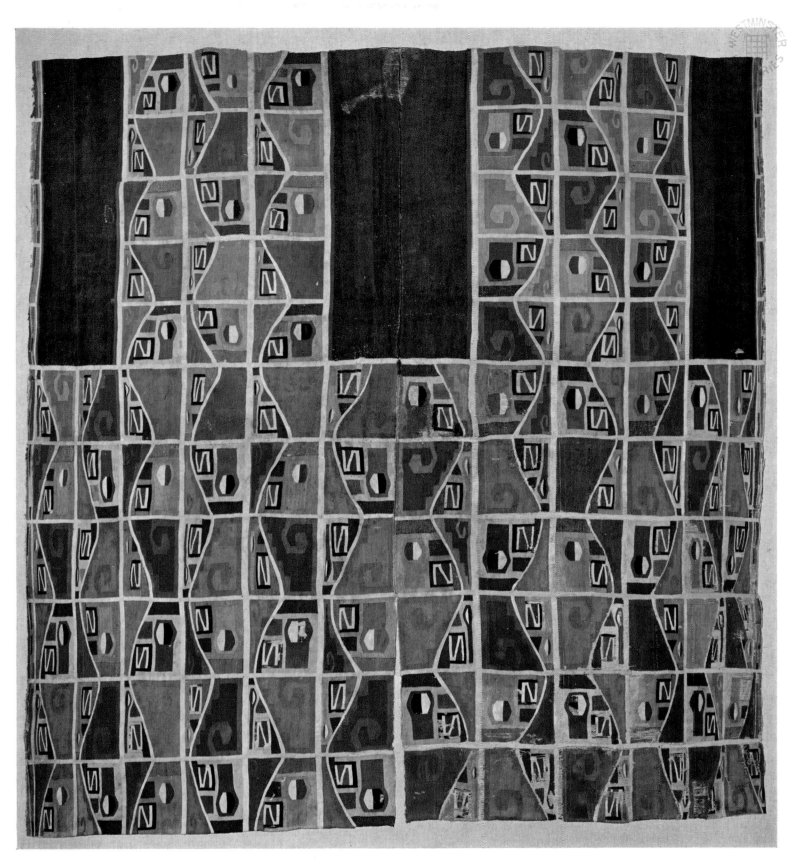

Poncho shirt. Coast of Peru. *Cat. No. 353.*

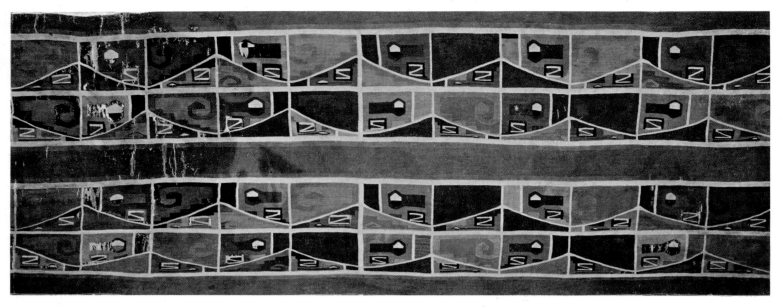

Portion of poncho shirt. Coast of Peru. *Cat. No. 354.*

Detail from *Cat. No. 354.*

Fragment of tapestry. Coast of Peru. *Cat. No. 355.*

Fragment of tapestry. South coast of Peru. *Cat. No. 356.*

Mantle or wall hanging. South coast of Peru. *Cat. No. 357.*

Detail from Plate CLII.

Three square hats of pile cloth. South coast of Peru. *Cat. Nos. 358–360.*

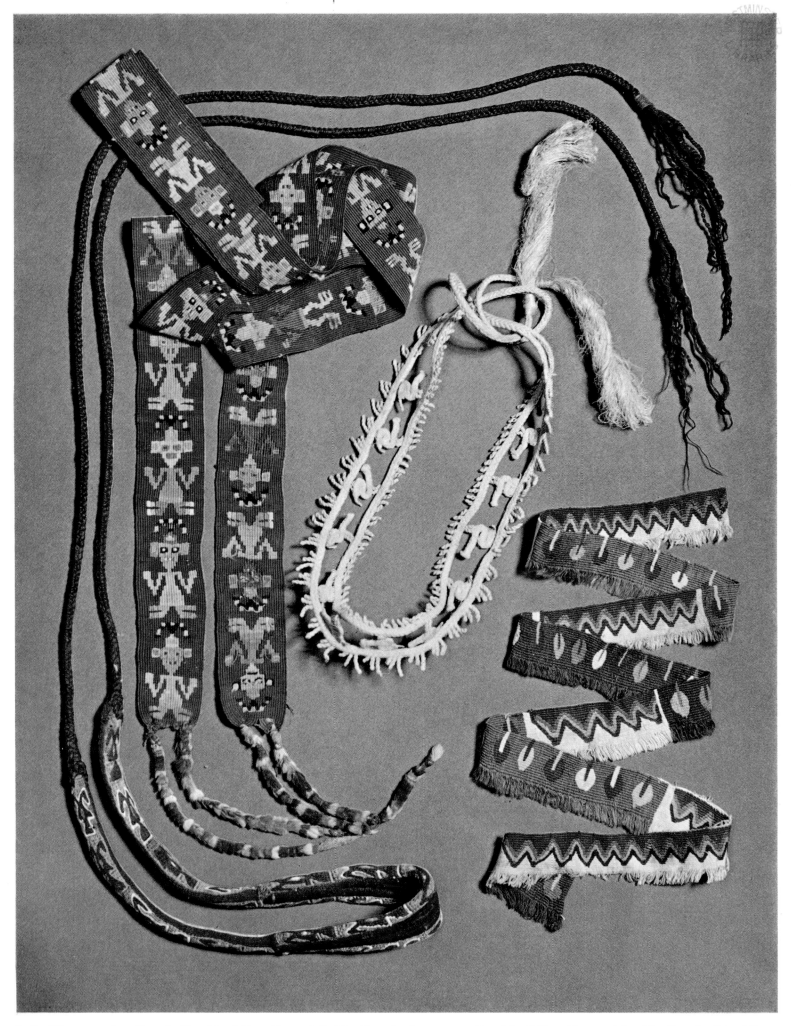

Left: Slit center headband. *Cat. No. 361.*—*Center left:* Headband of tapestry. *Cat. No. 363.*—*Center right:* Headband of braiding. *Cat. No. 362.*—*Right:* Border fragment of tapestry. *Cat. No. 364.* Coast of Peru.

Detail of a mantle. Central coast of Peru. *Cat. No. 365.*

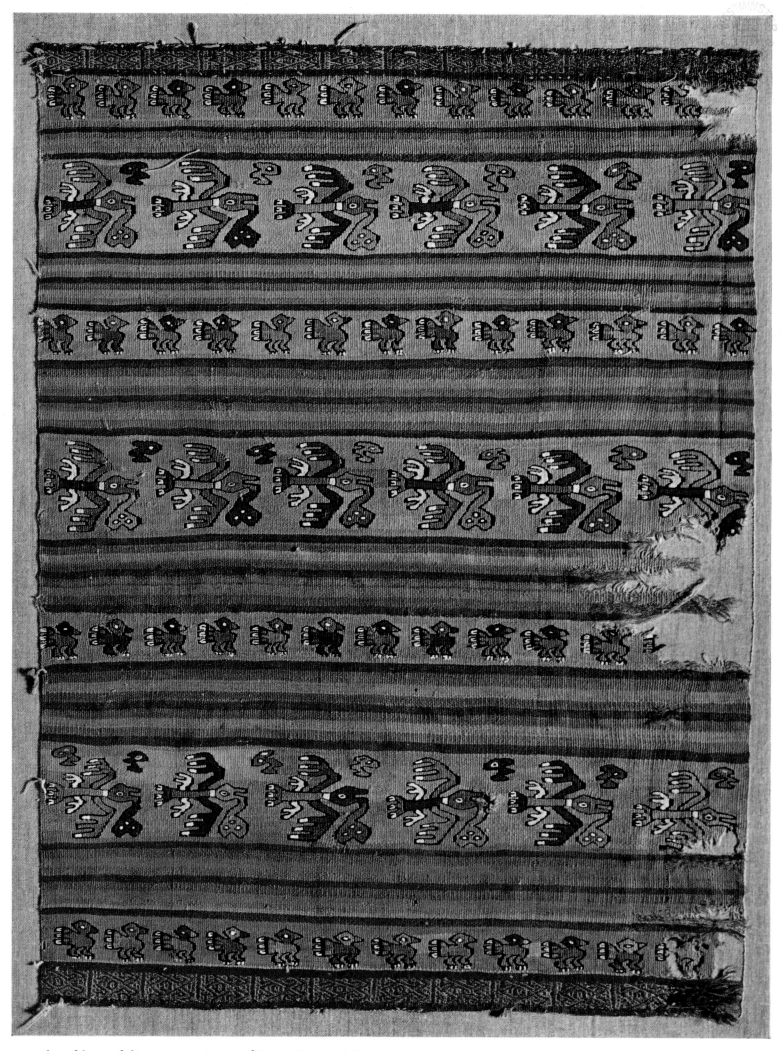

Complete fabric of slit tapestry. Coast of Peru. *Cat. No. 368.*

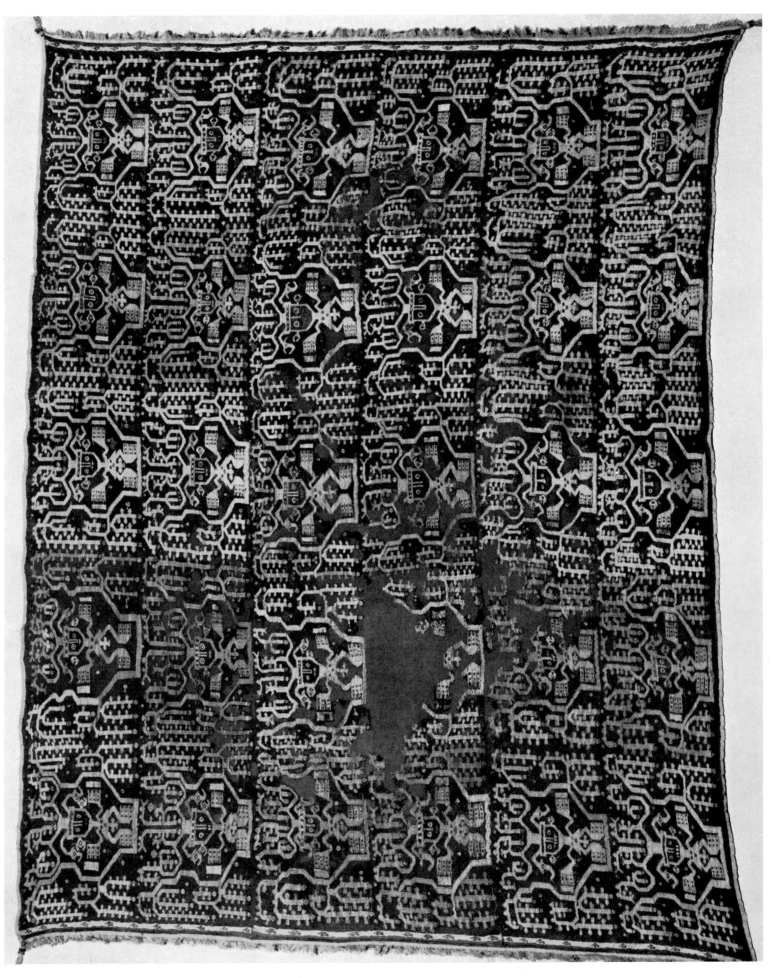

Large embroidered mantle, shawl or cloak. North coast of Peru. *Cat. No. 370.*

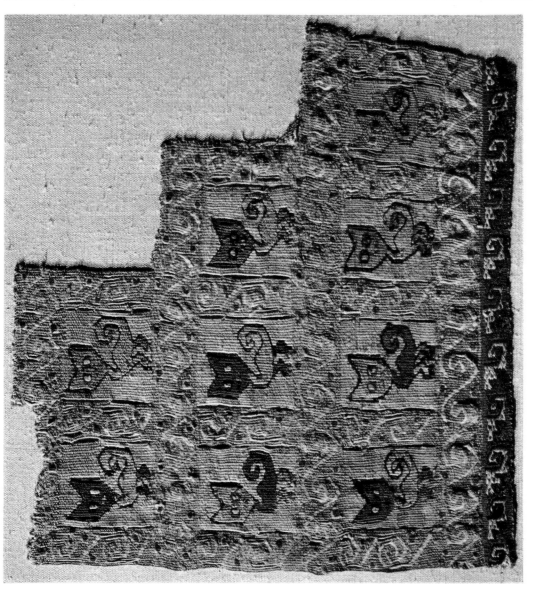

Fragment of the corner of a shawl(?). Central coast of Peru. *Cat. No. 367.*

Fragment of split tapestry. Central coast of Peru. *Cat. No. 369.*

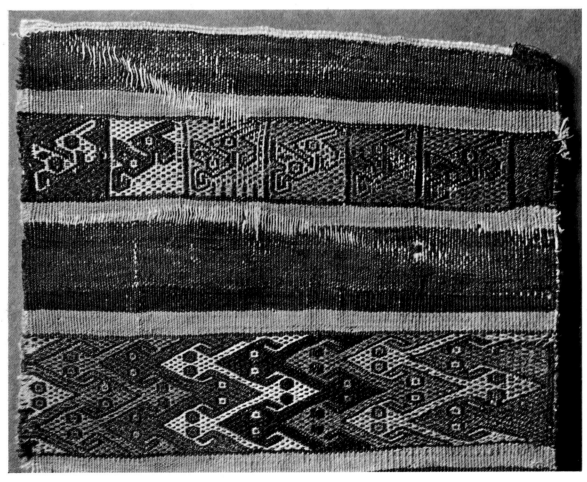

Fragment of interlocked weft pattern. Central coast of Peru. *Cat. No. 371.*

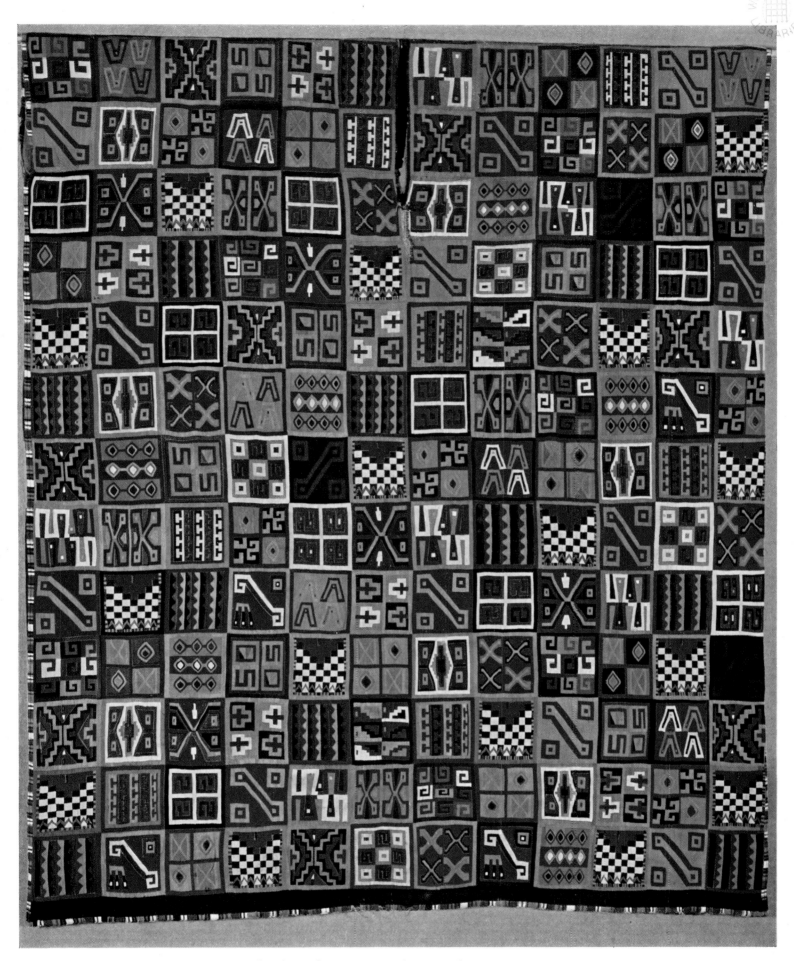

Poncho shirt of tapestry. South coast of Peru. *Cat. No. 373.*

Poncho shirt of tapestry. Coast of Peru. *Cat. No. 372.*

CATALOGUE

Drawing of the Slate Mirror-Back, Cat. No. 20-A.
By Miguel Covarrubias.

CATALOGUE

Numbers in brackets following the Catalogue numbers refer to
Indigenous Art of the Americas, Collection of Robert Woods Bliss,
National Gallery of Art, Washington, D.C., 1947.

CENTRAL AND EASTERN MEXICO

ARCHAIC CULTURE

See p. 15 and map at end of book.

I

CLAY FIGURINE typical of the earliest plastic art in Mexico.
Tlatilco, Mexico, D. F. Height, ca. 3¾ in. Pl. I, *top left.*

2

HEAD OF A FIGURINE. As in a Picasso drawing, two mouths, two noses and three eyes suggest motion. The Hindu deity Siva also is shown with three eyes, representing insight into the past, present and future.
Tlatilco, Mexico, D. F. Height, 1⅝ in. Pl. I, *top center.*

OLMEC CULTURE

See p. 15

3

JADEITE PENDANT representing a human head with a mask which suggests a duck bill covering the lower part of the face. This piece recalls the head of the famous Tuxtla statuette, at one time thought to carry the earliest date recorded in the Maya calendar system.
Mexico. Height, 3¼ in. Pl. I, *bottom left.*

4

JADEITE PENDANT representing a man with a greatly enlarged head. This is of the so-called 'baby-face' type, characteristic of Olmec sculpture, which depicts an anthropomorphic jaguar. Such faces have elongated and sometimes insloping eyes, broad feline noses, fat lips and an open mouth with a pendicle in the center and turned-down corners. The finely incised details are typical of the style.
Mexico. Height, ca. 3⅜ in. Pl. I, *bottom center.*

5

JADEITE STANDING HUMAN FIGURE who holds on his chest objects indicated by incised lines. These may represent a circular shield and a bundle of darts.
San Cristobal Tepatlaxco, Puebla, Mexico. Height, 4⅜ in. Pl. I, *bottom right.*

6–7

JADEITE 'STILETTOS' representing the head and beak of a bird, perhaps a humming-bird. Details of the feathers appear on the handle of the larger piece. They are classed as Olmec on account of the quality of the stone and the characteristic fine incising.

For a period of many centuries, the peoples of central and southern Mexico as well as the Maya performed cruel acts of self-mutilation and penance by offering their own blood to the gods, drawn chiefly from the tongue or ears. The cutting usually was done with an obsidian knife, but there is pictorial evidence that ropes or rods with attached cactus spines were passed through perforated tongues. It has been suggested that nos. 6 and 7 are specialized tools for the ceremonial drawing of blood.

We should also note that native codices of later date illustrate the ceremonial piercing of ears or septum of the nose to insert insignia of rank. The two jade specimens may have served this purpose.

The large specimen is from *southern Vera Cruz, Mexico.* Lengths, ca. 6¾ and 2⅝ in. Pl. I, *upper right.*

8 (129)

STANDING FIGURE OF A MAN. The material is highly polished diopside-jadeite. A small breech clout is the only clothing and the body is strongly muscled. Frontal deformation of the skull is evident. The hands once held something, as a hole is drilled through each. There also are small holes in the ear lobes for the attachment of ornaments.
Mexico. Height, 9⅛ in. Pl. II.

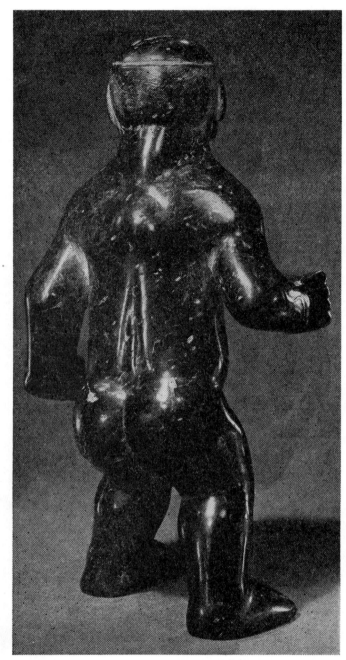

Fig. 10. *Back of Olmec serpentine statuette.* (Cat. No. 10.)

9

BLUE JADEITE BUST OF A MAN. This small fragment, probably part of a standing figurine, represents Olmec art at its best – from a Europeanized point of view. The simplicity and strength of the modelling are of monumental quality.
Mexico. Height, 2¾ in. Pl. III.

10

STANDING FEMALE FIGURE OF SERPENTINE, portraying an aged female with pendant breasts. She wears a jaguar mask. The eyes were insets and there are raised

undulating lines on the outside of each arm. The soles of the feet were carved to indicate a high arch. This results in a conventionalized type of footprint which also is found in the Teotihuacan (Pl. XXV) and Aztec periods. *Tabasco, Mexico.* Height, ca. 7⅜ in. Pl. IV, fig. 10.

11

SERPENTINE STATUETTE which represents a man clad as a jaguar. The hands are clearly human and the body muscles represent a man rather than a beast. The eyes were insets and there are holes for insets in the ears, backs of the hands and tops of the feet. This piece is reported to have been found with the preceding specimen. Both may represent masked dancers.
Tabasco, Mexico. Height, ca. 3⅛ in. Pl. V.

12

SERPENTINE PENDANT representing a dancer doing an entrechat. This piece was broken across the shoulder long ago. The two parts were discovered several years apart.
San Cristobal Tepatlaxco, Puebla, Mexico. Height, ca. 4⅜ in. Pl. VI, *top right.*

13

SMALL PENDANT OF DIOPSIDE-JADEITE in the form of a 'baby face' head.
Mexico. Height, 1¾ in. Pl. VI, *bottom.*

14

ANGULAR MASK OF TREMOLITE, representing a 'baby face'. The term *mask* applied to such flat heads is a misnomer because, having no eye holes, they could not have been worn except as a gorget. The term, however, has the authority of long usage in Mexican archaeology. It is possible that they were parts of composite statues of wood and stone. It has been established that this type of head is a humanized jaguar head and at times it appears on a jaguar body.
Mexico. Height, 3¾ in. Pl. VI, *top left.*

15

MASK OF BROWN MARBLE representing a jaguar head. This piece is not of typical Olmec style, but it has been placed in that period because its vigor and simplicity suggest an early date.
Rio Balsas, Guerrero, Mexico. Width, 7 in. Pl. VII.

16 (130)

MASK OF ROCK QUARTZ AND CHALCEDONY representing a jaguar. The prominence of the canines is uncommon in Olmec art, but the flame-like incised eyebrows are very typical.
Rio Balsas, Guerrero, Mexico. Height, 6 in. Pl. VIII, top.

16-A

LARGE POTTERY HEAD with the skull elongated by artificial deformation. The narrow face and prominent cheeks recall a type of Veracruz *hacha* (Pl. XX), usually considered to be of Late Classic date, but skull deformation is not a characteristic of this style.
Olmec (?). Mexico. Height, 5½ in. Pl. VIII, bottom.

17

PAIR OF DIOPSIDE-JADEITE CELTS. These brilliantly colored pieces probably were ceremonial insignia or perhaps were used to cut up food by hand. They are too heavy to be of service if hafted.
Rancho Potrerillos, El Mangal, Vera Cruz, Mexico. Lengths, 8$\frac{7}{16}$, 11$\frac{1}{8}$ in. Pl. IX, bottom.

17-A

JADEITE SPEAR-THROWER. The function of spear-throwers is explained in connection with Aztec and Peruvian examples (nos. 65 and 319; Pls. XLIX and CXXXI). From the quality of the stone, this example probably is of Olmec manufacture and therefore may well be the oldest now known in the New World. It also probably is the longest existing piece of carved jade.
The shaft of this spear-thrower is round except for the loops and the peg at one end. This end terminates with a short groove cut to accommodate the shaft of the spear. While the total length is sufficient for an effective weapon, the loops are too small to insert adult fingers. This must indicate that the object is ceremonial rather than utilitarian.
Olmec culture (?). State of Vera Cruz, Mexico. Length, 22½ in. Pl. IX, top center.

17-B

JADEITE SPEAR-THROWER. This specimen, reported to have been found with no. 17A, is shorter and of somewhat different type. It also has a peg at one end and the adjacent portion of the shaft is flattened to accommodate the spear. The finger loops, however, are lacking, but there are grooves where we would expect them to be.

This suggests that loops of some other material, such as shell, bone, wood or leather, once were lashed to the shaft. These may have been of sufficient size to insert the fingers, but the shaft is too short for an effective weapon. Ceremonial use is again implied.
Olmec culture (?). Vera Cruz, Mexico. Length, 13 in. Pl. IX, top left.

17-C

JADEITE CHOPPING KNIFE. This is a thin slab with a sharp blade at the lower end which shows slight signs of use. While many of the artifacts usually classed as celts or axes actually were hafted, others were held in the hand and used for cutting relatively soft materials such as meat. This is a matter not of conjecture but of observation. In the present instance the blade is too thin for hafting except for a ceremonial purpose.
Olmec culture (?). Vera Cruz, Mexico. Length, 11 in. Pl. IX, top right.

18 (131)

PORPHYRY MASK representing a jaguar with no lower jaw. There are sockets for inlays on the cheeks and forehead.
Southern Vera Cruz, Mexico. Width, 5$\frac{3}{8}$ in. Pl. X, center.

19

PAIR OF TUBULAR BEADS of diopside-jadeite.
Mexico. Lengths, 6$\frac{7}{16}$, 5$\frac{5}{8}$ in. Pl. X, top and right.

20 (47)

BREAST PLATE OF DIOPSIDE-JADEITE. This piece is placed with the Olmec group on account of the type of incising. The design itself, however, is found on Teotihuacan pottery (Pl. XXXI, top). Holes on the back indicate the plaque was suspended horizontally.
Mexico. Length, 6½ in. Pl. X, bottom.

CLASSIC VERACRUZ
See p. 17

20-A

SLATE MIRROR-BACK carved in typical Classic Veracruz style. The reflecting surface is of hematite, not mounted as a mosaic (Pl. CXXVI) but a combination of minerals occurring in nature.
The central figure is a kneeling man clad in a breechclout, adorned by a necklace and ear disk. The elaborate

Fig. 11. *Details of stone yoke illustrated in Pl. xii.*
(Cat. No. 21).

arrangement of the hair recalls the Maya figurines of
Jaina and Jonuta styles (Pl. LXIX). From his mouth
issues a 'speech scroll'. Evidently he is addressing the
small bird in front of his face. Fixed forms of this device
acquired definite meanings in later times in Mexico,
but we have no indication what is being said in this case.
Surrounding the man and bird is an intricate abstract
pattern of scrolls. These are of the kind presumed to be
early, typically found on stone yokes (Pl. XII), although
sometimes seen on *hachas* (Pl. XVII, *top*). It is a tribute to
the skill of the artist that he could successfully apply

such complex traditional motifs to decorative fields of
such radically different shape.
*Early Classic Veracruz style. Vega de la Torre, State of
Vera Cruz, Mexico. Diam., 4⅞ in. Pl. XI and page 232.*

21

YOKE OF DIORITE PORPHYRY. A human head with
elaborate headdress occurs on the top of the arch. On the
shoulders are arms and hands, the latter holding scrolls.
Legs and feet appear on the sides. The outer corners are
adorned with human faces surmounted by elaborate
headdress. In style, the scrolls place this piece as Late
Classic. Simplified treatment of the faces vaguely recalls
stone masks of Teotihuacan style (Pl. XXVIII).
*Mexico. Length, 17¼ in.; width, 15¹⁄₁₆ in.; height, 4½ in.
Pl. XII, fig. 11.*

22

STONE YOKE OF METADIORITE. In contrast to the
previous specimen, this example is carved with extreme
simplicity.
*Near the city of Vera Cruz, Mexico. Length, 15⅜ in.;
width, 13⅜ in.; height, 4⁵⁄₁₆ in. Pl. XIII.*

23 (105)

HACHA OF MARBLE. The top and left side form a blade,
suggesting a ceremonial axe, but the notch in the right
side of the base has a flat and rough surface, indicating
attachment, perhaps to a broad belt. The carved figure
may represent an acrobat or a so-called Diving god.
*Central Vera Cruz, Mexico. Style of Veracruz. Height,
12 in. Pl. XV.*

23-A

HACHA OF MARBLE with cut-out background. This
technique is not common but another example is seen
in Pl. XV. At the bottom is a bearded head. As the
lips are partially open and the eyes appear to be closed,
this may portray a trophy head. There are large disks
attached to the ear lobes. A triple cord droops from the
top of the ears across the cheeks and crosses the bridge of
the nose. Its nature is not clear.
Above the head is the squatting figure of an animal with
a front paw replaced by a human hand. Small ornaments
are attached to the face and hand, below which is a round
dot. With considerable hesitation, we identify the animal
as a dog, symbol of the Aztec day *Itzcuintli* and the
Yucatacan Maya *Oc*, and the dot then may represent the
numeral One. We should add that the style of the animal

is not in accord with contemporary local tradition and may be the result of intrusive foreign influence.

If this dubious interpretation can be accepted, this specimen is an early manifestation of the calendar in general use throughout the central Mexican plateau several centuries after the accepted stylistic date of this piece (fig. 14). This possibility is enhanced by the fact that the date '13 Rabbit' is recorded on the walls of El Tajin, which is regarded as Late Classic Veracruz. In this case, the numerals are of Maya type. Rabbit, however, was a day symbol on the Mexican mainland but not among the Maya.

Late Classic Veracruz. State of Vera Cruz, Mexico. Height, 13⅞ in. Pl. XIV.

24

BASALT HACHA, representing a dead warrior's head in an eagle mask. Only the closed eyes, nose and lips of the human face appear. Top and forehead of the mask form a dull blade. The scrolls suggest a Late Classic date.
Mexico. Style of Veracruz. Height, 13½ in. Pl. XVI.

25 (103)

HACHA OF MARBLE, perhaps representing a bat. The specimens previously considered consisted of two profiles on very thin slabs. This example, while retaining the blade-like forehead, also shows the snout and jaws full-face. This tendency to widen the face and to round the forehead continues until sculpture in the full round is attained. At the same time, the group unity is maintained by the notched base indicating similar function. This specimen, on the basis of scroll type, is one of the few examples in the collection to which an Early Classic date has been attributed.
Mexico. Height, 8½ in. Pl. XVII, *top.*

26 (104)

HACHA OF MARBLE, representing a helmeted warrior wearing a nose ring. Like the preceding piece, this example illustrates the widening of the full-face aspect.
Mexico. Height, 10 in. Pl. XVII, *bottom.*

27 (99)

HACHA OF BASALT, depicting a vulture. The forehead can no longer be considered a rudimentary blade, but may be described as a ridge or bevel. The arched back

suggests that this form may be intermediate between the thin *hacha* and wide *palma* groups of sculpture. This large and heavy piece evidently needed firm support, for the entire base has been left unpolished.
State of Vera Cruz, Mexico. Height, 13½ in. Pl. XVIII.

27-A

METADIORITE HACHA of the thick, semi-three-dimensional type, discussed in connection with no. 25. The eyes and nose apparently are human. A large ring is clipped to the septum of the nose. Below is an appendage which may represent a tongue, comparable to the tongue in Pl. XVII, *top.* Large spirals issue from the chin and cover the cheeks.

A massive headdress or helmet caps the head, with massive spirals on either side. Above these are eye sockets formerly inlaid with pyrites, and the semicircular slits in front must represent nostrils. The concept is that of a bird or turtle head. In that case, the curve of the beak suggests a parrot rather than an eagle, traditional headgear in Mexico. See Pl. XVI.
Classic Veracruz style. State of Vera Cruz, Mexico. Height, 6¾ in. Pl. XIX: views from front, top, and side.

28 (108)

CRESTED HEAD OF BASALT. This and the two following pieces are allied to the *hacha* type of sculpture on account of similar treatment of the base and of slight thinning of the face as viewed from in front. It will be noted that the eyes in each case are closed, the mouth slightly open and the lips flabby. This suggests decapitation and human sacrifice, a rite depicted elsewhere in Late Classic Veracruz sculpture. All three specimens have similar hair arrangements consisting of a row of pompoms running back from the forehead and larger patches over the ears, probably an indication of the ceremony during which victims were killed.
Central Vera Cruz, Mexico. Height, 5¾ in. Pl. XX.

29 (107)

CRESTED HEAD OF ONYX MARBLE. This piece is similar to no. 28 except that the mouth is wide open and a nose ring is shown.
Central Vera Cruz, Mexico. Height, 6⅜ in. Pl. XXI.

30 (106)

CRESTED HEAD OF MARBLE. Again the subject is the head of a dead man with open mouth and closed eyes.

Details differ, such as the treatment of the hair crest. The width of the face has been made progressively greater until it can be regarded as of natural proportions. *Central Vera Cruz, Mexico.* Height, 6⅜ in. Pl. XXII.

31

PALMATE STONE OF DIORITE. This carving has an arched base in contrast to the notched base of the *hachas;* the back, instead of being relatively narrow, is flaring. The subject is a vulture, rendered in the three-quarters round. Perhaps it represents a vulture mask, for a collar of square plaques implies human use. The back seems to represent upraised wings, but the central notch is typical of the style regardless of the subject. Although many palmate stones exhibit scroll patterns, it is believed that the group as a whole is of later date than most of the stone yokes and *hachas.*
Vicinity of Puebla, Mexico. Height, 6¾ in. Pl. XXIII.

32

POTTERY HEAD, representing a dead warrior wearing an eagle mask. The same subject is shown in stone in Pl. XVI, which probably dates from a later period. Characteristic features are the closed eyes and open mouth. The eagle beak and one eye have been broken and lost.
Remojadas style. Vera Cruz, Mexico. Height, 12⅛ in. Pl. XXIV.

TEOTIHUACAN CULTURE

See p. 17

33 (124)

FRESCO found at Tetitla near Teotihuacan, Mexico. This is one of a pair which flanked a door. The color and style are typical of Classic Teotihuacan art. The scene, although complicated by the introduction of obscure symbolism, is essentially simple. Along the base runs a road, marked as such by footprints. This leads, at the left, to the door of a temple. The temple stands on a platform. It has both rectangular and triangular moldings, also a tall and elaborately adorned roof.
At the right there is a richly dressed individual disguised as a jaguar, who bends one knee to the ground. He wears a huge feather headdress and carries a rattle set on a shaft as well as a shield, both adorned with plumes. His legs and body are encased in a net. A large scroll in front of the face represents speech.
The costume, consisting of a net, makes it possible to identify the individual as a priest of the Rain god known

as Tlaloc to the Aztec many centuries later. Evidently he is about to enter the temple to pray. Across the background of this scene run a series of parallel diagonal lines with pointed fringes attached. This well may symbolize the sought-for rain.
Tetitla, Mexico, D. F. 28⅝ × 83⅝ in. Pls. XXV–XXVI.

34 (120)

LARGE MASK OF BLACK LIMESTONE. Fractures show that the entire surface originally was black, but it has now corroded to the present gray color. Originally there must have been inset eyes and teeth.
Heads of this type have been found at the ancient city of Teotihuacan and elsewhere in central Mexico and are attributed to the Classic period of the Teotihuacan style. Their function is unknown, but it is evident that they were attached to something, for the backs are hollowed and holes in pairs pierce the back edges.
Mexico. Height, 9¾ in.; width, 10 in. Pl. XXVII and fig. 12.

Fig. 12. *Profile of limestone mask* illustrated in Pl. XXVII. Style of Teotihuacan. (Cat. No. 34.)

35

LARGE MASK OF ONYX MARBLE. The stone is of unusually fine quality and has retained its high polish. The eyes were inlays, traces of which still remain. A notch in the forehead is an unusual feature.
Mexico. Style of Teotihuacan. Height, ca. $7\frac{1}{10}$ *in. Frontispiece.*

36 (121)

LARGE MASK OF GREEN SERPENTINE. This piece evidently belongs to the same period and style as the preceding specimen. Traces of the inlay of eyes and mouth indicate the use of iron pyrites which has turned to rust.
Mexico. Height, $8\frac{1}{2}$ *in. Pl. XXVIII.*

37

SMALL MASK OF JADEITE. The acorn shape, the type of headdress or helmet and the mouth cut through to the back make this piece unique. The sharpness of lips and eyelids as well as the delicate plastic quality of the face places it as Classic Teotihuacan.
There is no record of where this specimen was found, but it is known that it formerly belonged to President Porfirio Díaz, whose widow sold it in Paris where it was subsequently acquired by the late Joseph Brummer. Mr. Brummer refused to part with it during his lifetime, but it has repeatedly appeared in loan exhibitions and has been previously illustrated many times. It first appears in color in this volume.
Mexico. Height, ca. $2\frac{3}{4}$ *in. Pl. XXIX.*

38 (93)

ONYX MARBLE MASK, showing the imprint of the cloth with which it was buried. This and the specimen in Pl. XXI are among the oldest known examples of carvings in this material, which came into common use in later times (Pls. LI–LIII).
Mexico. Height, 6 in.; width, $5\frac{1}{2}$ *in. Pl. XXX, top.*

39

SMALL MOTTLED STONE MASK. This little specimen resembles the larger masks found at Teotihuacan.
State of Guerrero, Mexico. Height, ca. $2\frac{3}{4}$ *in. Pl. XXX, center right.*

40

JADE HEAD OF THE MEXICAN FIRE GOD. The Aztec rightly named this deity Huehueteotl, 'very old god', for not only is he represented as aged, but his worship can be traced back to the Archaic period (p. 15). His likeness first became common at Teotihuacan. In Aztec times, a cruel ceremony was performed in his honor during which bound captives were cast on burning coals before extracting their hearts.
Mexico. Height, ca. $2\frac{3}{8}$ *in. Pl. XXX, center left.*

41

CROSS-LEGGED, SEATED FIGURE OF DIORITE PORPHYRY. In addition to certain monumental carvings and stone masks, small stone figurines are found at Teotihuacan. These, like the masks, show extreme simplicity and lack the ritual trappings portrayed on the larger sculptures and most of the pottery figurines.
Mexico. Height, 5 in. Pl. XXX, bottom center.

42, 43 (41, 42)

PAIR OF EAGLE HEADS OF DIOPSIDE-JADEITE, exhibiting traces of red paint.
Rio Balsas, Guerrero, Mexico. Lengths, $2\frac{1}{16}$, $2\frac{1}{8}$ *in. Pl. XXX, bottom right and left.*

44

POTTERY JAR OF BROWN-WARE with cover, both stucco-coated and painted. The motif on the cover, also repeated on the side walls, combines the mouth of Tlaloc, the Rain god, with the plumed headdress of Ehecatl-Quetzalcoatl, the Wind god. Both these deities were worshipped by the Aztec in later times, but they had received homage, and their portrayal had become stylized nearly a thousand years before the Aztec rise to power.
A second motif (Pl. XXXI, *top*) alternates with the first on the side walls. The base element apparently terminates in feathers. It is repeated in a jade slab (Pl. X, *bottom*) which is drilled to hang horizontally. The curious elements at the top perhaps represent tie strings for a gorget. (See Pl. XXXV, *bottom left*.)
Vicinity of San Juan Teotihuacan, Mexico. Style of Teotihuacan. Height, including cover, $8\frac{1}{8}$ *in. Pl. XXXI.*

45 (125)

PLASTER-COATED BROWN-WARE POTTERY JAR with a complex painted design. This represents a plumed serpent, the head of which is in the center of Pl. XXXII, *bottom*. Flanking the neck is what appears to be a pair of short wings. To the left of the mouth is a large scroll, a convention for indicating speech which persisted until the Conquest in Mexico and spread southward to Central

America. This device, which seems to have originated at Teotihuacan, may be compared to the contemporary custom in cartoons of outlining words and attaching them to the speaker's mouth.

The serpent body, seen at the *top* of the same plate, runs horizontally and then downward so that it forms a dividing band between the two occurrences of the design. It is outlined by rows of feathers. Originally there were three legs, now broken.

Vicinity of San Juan Teotihuacan, Mexico. Style of Teotihuacan. Height, 4¾ in. Pl. XXXII.

(This and nos. 46–48 are said to have come from the same tomb, probably located in central Mexico.)

46 (126)

BROWN-WARE FRESCOED JAR set on open-work tripod legs. The subject seems to be a profile feathered serpent. An alternative interpretation of both this and no. 45 is that they portray a masked individual with a feathered 'pigtail' attached to the mask.

Vicinity of San Juan Teotihuacan, Mexico. Style of Teotihuacan. Height, 5¼ in. Pl. XXXIII, *top*.

47 (128)

BROWN-WARE FRESCOED TRIPOD JAR. The legs have pressed designs. The outer walls are divided into two tapering bands, one plastered and painted green, the other incised. The principal motif, one unit of which appears on the left side of the illustration, represents the upper jaw and snout of an animal – as attested by effigy vessels modelled in the round from Oaxaca.

Vicinity of San Juan Teotihuacan, Mexico. Height, 4⁷⁄₁₆ in. Pl. XXXIII, *bottom left*.

48 (127)

THIN ORANGE-WARE FRESCOED TRIPOD BOWL. The legs are not decorated, but a series of molded heads encircle the base of the walls. The principal motif consists of a face, which, as in Pl. XXXII, *bottom*, combined the fanged mouth of Tlaloc, the Rain god, with the plumed headdress of Quetzalcoatl, the Feathered Serpent.

Vicinity of San Juan Teotihuacan, Mexico. Style of Teotihuacan. Height, 4⅛ in. Pl. XXXIII, *bottom right*.

49

THIN ORANGE-WARE FRESCOED BOWL. This piece is very different from the preceding examples of Teotihuacan pottery, for the design is painted in red on pink rather than black over various colors. The exterior carries two major motifs, each repeated twice. One (Pl. XXXIV, *bottom*) had been identified as a butterfly. The other (*top*) represents a deity whose headdress is crowned by a butterfly design. He (or she?) stands with outspread arms and with hands grasping a staff. Around the neck is a necklace supporting a large gorget adorned with the head of an owl. The plaster has chipped off so that details of the feet cannot be observed. The entire interior was once plaster-coated and painted, but this has been destroyed so that no details are observable except the stylized band seen in the illustration.

Vicinity of San Juan Teotihuacan, Mexico. Style of Teotihuacan. Diam., 9⅝ in. Pl. XXXIV.

AZTEC CULTURE

See p. 21

50

KNEELING FIGURE OF DARK GREEN DIORITE representing Chalchihuitlicue, Aztec Water goddess, 'Our Lady of the Turquoise Skirt'. Whereas Tlaloc, the Rain god, governed growth and vegetation, Chalchihuitlicue ruled the rivers and lakes and was associated with an important cult. She is represented as a young girl who wears a poncho with points at the back and front. She also is marked by a peculiar arrangement of the hair with trimmed tassels hanging over the shoulders. Formerly in possession of President Porfirio Díaz.

Valley of Mexico. Aztec style. Height, 5 in. Pl. XXXV, *right*.

51 (111)

ANOTHER STATUE REPRESENTING CHALCHIHUITLICUE, Aztec goddess of Water. This piece is of basalt with traces of red paint. The two specimens differ in details of the ponchos and headdresses.

Mexico. Aztec style. Height, 6¾ in. Pl. XXXV, *left*.

52

STONE STATUE OF THE AZTEC GODDESS TLAZOLTEOTL (Eater of Filth) in the act of childbirth. This savage and emotional piece, which was first published nearly fifty years ago, is generally regarded as one of the finest extant examples of Aztec sculpture. Previously classified as wernerite, the stone from which this statue is carved is now identified as aplite speckled with garnets.

According to rumor, this carving was brought to France

Fig. 13. *Aztec Birth goddess* as shown in the Codex Borbonicus.
Drawing by Miguel Covarrubias.

mankind. Her priests heard confessions and granted absolution after due penance. As individuals could confess but once in a lifetime, they waited until old age.

Tlazolteotl also was adored as an Earth goddess in whose honor a girl impersonator was decapitated. Sometimes the goddess was portrayed wearing the skin of the victim (fig. 13) somewhat in the fashion the god Xipe was represented (no. 58).

Furthermore, Tlazolteotl was regarded as the goddess of childbirth. She was held to be the mother of Centeotl, the Maize god, and of Xochiquetzal, goddess of Fertility, Flowers and Weaving. The statue here discussed may commemorate the birth of one of these deities. At any rate, in addition to hearing confessions and granting absolutions, her priests had the important functions of casting the horoscopes and of naming the new-born.

In the native codices Tlazolteotl is depicted wearing elaborate regalia. These include a headdress of unspun cotton in which two spindles are stuck. Her nose is painted black and carries a peculiar pendant which covers the mouth. Also she wears sandals and ear disks with danglers of unspun cotton. These features appear in fig. 13. Examination of the statue reveals minute V-shaped holes in the hair, ear lobes, angle of the jaws, buttocks and ankles. These probably were made with cactus spines and served to attach adornments of perishable nature.

Mexico. Aztec culture. Height, ca. $8\frac{1}{8}$ in. Pls. XXXVI and XXXVII.

by one of the officers who served in Mexico during the Maximilian regime. It was discovered in an antique store in Paris and purchased by M. Damour, not for a geological collection as has been stated, but for what has been described as a 'magnifique collection des pierres dures travaillées'.

After M. Damour's death, the statue was acquired by Dr. Ribemont-Dessaignes, not as a fee from an impoverished patient, as legend would have it, but as a purchase. The doctor was a friend of the archaeologist E. T. Hamy, who was authorized to photograph and publish it (1906) and to make a replica for the Musée d'Ethnographie. Later, it was purchased from a dealer by Mr. Joseph Brummer, who brought it to the United States.

The goddess Tlazolteotl, also called Ixcuna or Ixcuina, had multiple functions in aboriginal Mexico. In addition to the Aztec she was worshipped by the Mixtec, Huastec and the historic Olmec (p. 15). In one aspect she was regarded as the goddess of carnal sin and licentiousness, but as the 'Eater of Refuse' she consumed the sins of

53

JADEITE FIGURE OF A SEATED RABBIT. It wears a broad belt adorned with skulls and crossbones, attached to the front of which is a warrior's head in an eagle helmet. The eyes were once inlaid.

To the Aztec, 'Rabbit' was the name of a day, in divination associated with good luck, fertility and the goddess Mayaúel. This deity symbolized the maguey plant, important in Aztec economy for its fibres, spines and intoxicating wine. Like the Ephesian Diana, the goddess had four hundred breasts to nourish her sons, the 'Four Hundred (i.e., innumerable) Rabbits', typifying the countless forms of drunkenness. These Rabbit gods were worshipped all over the Mexican plateau in many local guises and were associated with the harvest and the moon.

Drunkenness was a serious crime among the Aztec, except for the elders who had fulfilled their community obligations. Men over thirty were allowed moderate amounts to drink at festivals, but the young, regardless of rank, were punished for intoxication with penalties ranging from degradation to death.

The association of a god of Intoxication with the symbols

of death and the Eagle Knights society is not too clear under these circumstances. Perhaps this statue commemorates an occasion when the bars against intoxication were relaxed after a great victory.

Mexico. Aztec culture. Height, ca. 7⅛ in. Pls. XXXVIII and XXXIX.

54 (109)

COILED RATTLESNAKE OF RHYOLITE-PORPHYRY. A large part of the ritualistic art of Mexico and Central America is based on forms derived from serpents, particularly from the legendary feathered serpent known as Quetzalcoatl to the Aztec and Kukulcan to the Maya. There is little evidence of direct serpent worship or of the existence of serpent clans as among the Indians of our Southwest, notably the Hopi and Zuni.

The Aztec, however, are an exception to this statement, for, while they manufactured ritualistic serpents, they also turned out carvings of snakes with an obvious attempt at realism. Number 54 is a good example of this trend. Top and bottom it is shaped to represent the living venomous reptile of the countryside with its typical arrow-shaped head poised to strike. The only possible ceremonial feature consists of the rattles which are thirteen in number, and this was important in Mexican methods of divination.

Xochimilco, Valley of Mexico. Aztec culture. Diam., 24 in. Pls. XL and XLI, *top.*

55

SERPENT HEAD OF BLACK OLIVINE BASALT. In contrast to no. 54, this specimen has left the world of reality. Head and neck are clad in willowy feathers. Above the eye is a large 'supra-orbital plate', seen often in the art of other regions. The nostrils have become spirals, and great fangs protrude where they do not exist in nature. Finally, what looks like a ball held in the mouth is in fact a human face, battered beyond recognition. Serpents' heads of this type were often placed at the base of stairway balustrades.

Mexico. Aztec culture. Length, 14 1/16 in. Pl. XLI, *bottom.*

56 (110)

SERPENT OF QUARTZ-DIORITE. The top of the head, now broken, probably once was surmounted by a crest. Serpents of this type, called Xiucoatl by the Aztec, were associated with time and the New Year. The glyphs on the base of the snake denote the year 'Two Reed', above which appears the name of Montezuma II, who later was captured by Cortés (fig. 14, *bottom*).

Fig. 14. *The Aztec year 'Two Reed'*, corresponding to A.D. 1507, recorded on the base and back of specimens in Pls. XLII–XLIII. The former is surmounted by the crest of Montezuma II. (Cat. No. 56.)

The Aztec date 'Two Reed' corresponds to our A.D. 1507 and marks the last cyclical ceremony celebrated by the Aztec, who divided time into fifty-two-year periods corresponding in concept to our centuries. This and no. 57 are among the few dated Aztec pieces in the United States.

This specimen, it will be noted, presents a completely different concept of conventionalization from no. 55.

The body is no longer covered with feathers but with raised panels, bars and rows of dots. The fangs have become enormous and a pair of clawed legs have been added.

Mexico. Aztec culture. Diam., 17⅞ in. Pl. XLII, fig. 14.

57

MASK OF MOTTLED GREEN with a brown patina. Like the Teotihuacan masks, this is not a true mask, for there are no eye holes. The former (Pls. XXVII, XXVIII, XXIX) have the eye sockets and mouth left rough to hold inlays, but the pupils and teeth are incised in the Aztec mask with an attempt at realism. As is customary in Aztec and contemporary Mixtec art, only the upper teeth are shown. The carving in general is unusually delicate and shows details of the bone structure and headdress.

Like the Teotihuacan masks, this Aztec specimen is grooved on the back and has holes for suspension in the temples and ear lobes. In the case of the older masks we surmised that the stone heads might be part of composite statues. This is unlikely in the case of the Aztec mask, for, on the reverse side, the year 'Two Reed' or A.D. 1507 is recorded (fig. 14). The significance of that date has been discussed in connection with no. 56.

Mexico. Aztec culture. Height, 7¼ in. Pl. XLIII.

58

STATUETTE OF THE AZTEC GOD XIPE, clad in the skin of a sacrificed captive. This, to us, repulsive deity symbolized to the Aztec flowers and the renewal of vegetation in spring. He also was the patron of goldsmiths and the healer of inflamed eyes. His worship seems to have originated among the Mixtec or Zapotec in the south, but his cult had spread to central Mexico in Teotihuacan times, perhaps a thousand years before the Aztec rise to power. He also was known far to the south in El Salvador and Nicaragua, where Mexican colonies existed.

Victims sacrificed to Xipe were killed in one of two ways among the Aztec. Either the chest might be slit open and the still beating heart torn out or the individual might be lashed to a frame and pierced with arrows or darts so that his blood fertilized the earth.

Human sacrifice was widely spread in the New World. Both these Aztec ceremonies together with other details of ritual were known as far south as Colombia and, with some modifications, have been recorded in Peru. The arrow sacrifice existed as far north as our Plains area among the Pawnee.

Such widely distributed customs must be of great antiquity and today the point of origin is unknown. Human

sacrifice occasionally is recorded in the Classic art of the Maya area and Vera Cruz. In Toltec times, however, when most of the Aztec pantheon had been established, the importance of sacrifice greatly increased, and we begin to find special mounds with racks for preserving the skulls. Under the Aztec regime, human sacrifice assumed monstrous proportions, and thousands were killed during a single ceremony.

The Xipe statuette here illustrated represents an individual whose heart has been cut out. The body was then flayed and the skin was worn, for periods as long as a month, either by a priest or by the warrior who captured him.

It will be observed that the face, ears and part of the hair have been removed and are worn separately as a mask with the dead lips surrounding those of the living. The incision over the heart has been closed and a long cut made down the back. The body, arms and legs were then peeled, donned by the god impersonator and sewn up the back. The feet were not preserved, but the victim's hands usually were left attached to the skin of the forearm. The scalloped edges at the neck and ankles as well as the knots on the back are typical of such figures. Only a few statues are known, but Xipe is often depicted in native codices.

Tenango del Valle, Valley of Mexico. Height, ca. 9⅜ in. Pls. XLIV and XLV.

59

SMALL HEAD OF XIPE carved in shell. As in no. 58, the lips of the living and the dead are clearly distinguished. Ear ornaments and an elaborate headdress are shown. There are three circular symbols for jade on the headband.

Mexico. Height, 2⅛ in. Pl. XLVI, *center.*

60 (116)

SHELL NECKLACE representing eighteen skulls. The eyes are inlaid with hematite.

Found in a pottery jar near Texcoco, Valley of Mexico, with nos. 61, 72 and 73. Length, 16¾ in. Height of beads, ca. 15/16 in. Pl. XLVI.

61 (113)

MASSIVE SKULL OF OBSIDIAN. This piece, like the beads with which it was found (no. 60, Pl. XLVI) had the eyes and teeth cut with a tubular drill. It is reported that, when discovered, the sunken eye sockets were inlaid with blue and white shell. It was boiled, however, in order to clean it and the inlay disintegrated.

Death was such a commonplace in Aztec life that it is natural that it should be depicted in their art. Their gods demanded human sacrifice, and wars were waged more to secure victims than for conquest. Not only were sacrificial rites public affairs, but the skulls of the sacrificed were spitted on poles which were placed on racks near the principal temples.

Every Aztec child must have played around the base of these skull racks and may have grown up to feel that the skull had intrinsic beauty. More probably, however, this obsidian skull and other skulls illustrated in this catalogue and elsewhere are commemorative of feats of arms and subsequent sacrifice of important individuals. At any rate, it is clear that outstanding Aztec lapidaries labored to produce them.

Found in a pottery jar near Texcoco, Valley of Mexico, with nos. 60, 72, 73. Height, 4¼ in. Pl. XLVII.

62

CRYSTAL SKULL. This specimen is hollow and reflects exterior light. There is a hole in the top and presumably it was a pendant.

Mexico. Aztec culture. Height, 2¹¹⁄₁₆ in. Pl. XLVIII, top.

63

JADEITE SKULL. There are four holes for attachment at the back and a hole over one eye, perhaps for holding a feather.

Chalco, Valley of Mexico. Aztec culture. Height, 2½ in. Pl. XLVIII, bottom right.

64 (45)

JADEITE CUP with skull projecting from the side. This piece has apparently been broken and cut down in ancient times.

Valley of Mexico. Aztec culture. Height, 2⅝ in. Pl. XLVIII, bottom left.

65

CARVED WOODEN ATLATL OR SPEAR-THROWER. This was a device for increasing the leverage of the arm by lengthening it artificially. The butt of a light spear was placed against the peg seen in the upper left corner of the illustration so that in throwing a much larger arc was achieved. This weapon has been recorded in many parts of the world and generally is regarded as a more ancient invention than the bow and arrow.

The present specimen is adorned on its working face (*left*) by two rows of elongated plumed serpents and eagles. On the curved back, nine warriors are represented, some with spears and shields. All wear elaborate helmets, some of which are heads symbolizing the Eagle and the Jaguar Knights.

The history of this spear-thrower is not known. From the slight weathering of the very hard wood it seems probable that it had been concealed in a dry cave, but it may be part of the sixteenth-century loot. At any rate, this is the type of weapon with which the Aztec tried to oppose the army of Cortés.

Mexico. Aztec culture. Length, ca. 23¾ in. Pl. XLIX and fig. 15.

66 (88)

LABRET OF CRYSTAL with gold and silver tips. This is an ornament one end of which was inserted through a hole in the lower lip so that it hung over the chin. The inner end (Pl. L, *second row, left*) is of cast gold, the outer of hammered and soldered sheet silver. The crystal core may not be contemporaneous with the tips. Early accounts of Mexico mention bimetallic objects with admiration, but few are known today.

Mexico. Aztec culture. Length, 2⅞ in. Pl. L, second row, left.

67 (89)

GOLD LABRET in the form of an eagle head. Most Aztec labrets represent this bird, and it is possible that labrets were habitually worn only by the Eagle Knights.

Mexico. Aztec culture. Length, 1⅝ in. Pl. L, second row, right.

68

EAR SPOOL OF OBSIDIAN capped by a gold disk. Aztec lapidaries aroused the admiration of the Spaniards by the delicacy of their work. Among the finest surviving pieces are ear spools of brittle materials such as obsidian and crystal, often ground to paper thinness.

Mexico. Aztec culture. Diam. 1⅜ in. Pl. L, top right.

69 (87)

PAIR OF CRYSTAL EAR SPOOLS, both capped by a gold sheet.

Mexico. Aztec culture. Diam., 1 in. Pl. L, top center and second row center.

70 (86)

CRYSTAL EAR SPOOL.
Mexico. Aztec culture. Diam., 1⁵⁄₁₆ in. Pl. L, top left.

71

PAIR OF OBSIDIAN EAR SPOOLS. These specimens are unfinished, showing that the outer side was the last to be ground down and polished.

Mexico. Aztec culture. Diam., 1⁷⁄₁₆ in. Pl. L, third row.

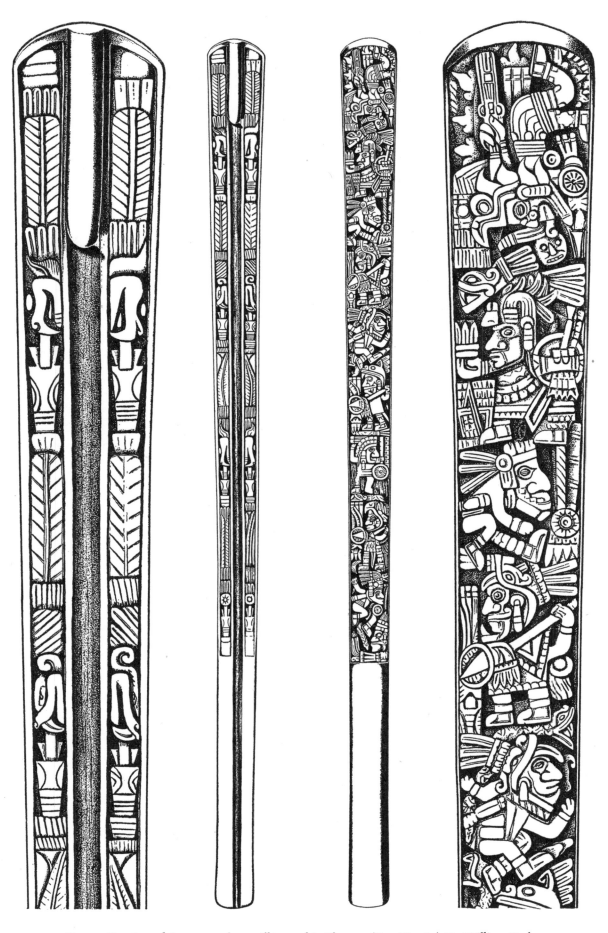

Fig. 15. *Drawings of Aztec spear-thrower* illustrated in Pl. XLIX. (Cat. No. 65.) By William Baake.

72

PAIR OF OBSIDIAN EAR SPOOLS. The extreme thinness and conical groove are unusual.
Found in a pottery jar near Texcoco, Valley of Mexico, with nos. 60, 61 and 73. Diam., $1\frac{9}{16}$ in. Pl. L, *bottom left and right.*

73

OBSIDIAN TUBE of unknown use.
Found in a pottery jar near Texcoco with nos. 60, 61 and 72. Length, $1\frac{15}{16}$ in. Pl. L, *bottom center.*

ONYX MARBLE JARS

See p. 23

74 (96)

ONYX MARBLE EFFIGY JAR representing a monkey. The tail, which encircles the vessel, is held over the head. A very similar jar of polished obsidian reputedly was dug up near Texcoco in the Valley of Mexico. This unusual pose, however, is most commonly found in the gold-work from the Province of Veraguas in Panama. As a number of gold ornaments from the Isthmus reached Mexico in trade, it is possible that the concept originated in the South.
The use of onyx marble for sculpture in Mexico extends back to the Classic Veracruz and Teotihuacan periods (Pls. XXI, XXX, *top*). It is uncertain, however, when vessels of onyx marble were first manufactured, but it is known that effigy forms were in use at the time of the Conquest because an example which never had been underground turned up in Spain. It is now in a private collection in England.
Mexico. Height, $12\frac{1}{2}$ in. Pl. LI.

75 (97)

FLARING ONYX MARBLE JAR with tripod legs. Thin and resonant. The horizontal striations are inherent in the stone, but the parallel vertical streaks are the marks of the tubular drilling by which the vessel was hollowed out.
State of Vera Cruz, Mexico. Height, ca. $9\frac{3}{8}$ in. Pl. LII, *top.*

76

LARGE CYLINDRICAL JAR OF ONYX MARBLE set on tripod legs. The marks of manufacture again are faintly visible as in no. 75.
Mexico. Height, $13\frac{1}{2}$ in. Pl. LII, *bottom.*

77 (98)

GLOBULAR TRIPOD JAR OF ONYX MARBLE. This small vessel clearly embodies the shape of a pottery prototype.
Mexico. Height, $5\frac{1}{2}$ in. Pl. LIII, *top.*

SOUTHERN MEXICO

See p. 23

78

NECKLACE of curiously shaped stone beads.
San Geronimo, Guerrero, Mexico. Length, ca. $23\frac{1}{2}$ in. Pl. XLVIII.

79

TUBULAR BAR PENDANT of jadeite.
State of Guerrero, Mexico. Length, ca. $9\frac{3}{8}$ in. Pl. LIV, *center.*

80

RECTANGULAR BAR PENDANT. This and the preceding specimen (79) were suspended from bead necklaces and worn horizontally across the chest. This specimen has four holes in the base for the attachment of danglers. Bar pendants were also worn in the Maya area, in Costa Rica and parts of Panama (Pl. XCII, *lower left*, and LXVIII, *lower right*).
Rio Balsas, State of Guerrero, Mexico. Length, $5\frac{15}{16}$ in. Pl. LV, *bottom.*

81

WINGED PENDANT of diopside-jadeite with four holes in the top for suspension. This type of pendant is known from Venezuela to Mexico. It represents a bat with extended wings, usually but not always with the head and body omitted. Costa Rican examples appear in Pl. XCI, *top* and Pl. XCVI, *top.*
Mexico. Length, $10\frac{1}{2}$ in. Pl. LIII, *bottom.*

82 (48)

PAIR OF QUARTZITE EAR DISKS. The backs and tubes to be inserted in the ears are unpolished.
Mexico. Width, $3\frac{1}{4}$ in. Pl. LVI, *bottom.*

83

SMALL STONE HEAD.
State of Guerrero, Mexico. Length, ca. $1\frac{3}{4}$ in. Pl. LIV, *center left.*

84

SMALL STONE HEAD.
State of Guerrero, Mexico. Length, 3⅞ in.
Pl. LIV, *bottom right.*

85

STONE HEAD. The modelling of the face, treatment of the ears and type of headdress are all unusual.
Mexico. Height, ca. 4 in. Pl. LIV, *top left.*

86

MARBLE HEAD. Most Mexican sculpture is formal, impersonal and static. This evidently was due to tradition, for emotion and movement are represented both in other media and occasionally in stone (Pl. VI, *top right,* and Pl. XI). This head is unusual because the individual is sucking in his lower lip.
Mexico. Height, 5¾ in. Pl. LVI, *top.*

87 (92)

DIOPSIDE-JADEITE HEAD. The curve of the lips and slant of the eyes suggest remote Olmec influence, but the fact that the pupil of the eye is carved rather than inlaid does not denote great antiquity.
Mexico. Height, 5 3/16 in. Pl. LV, *top.*

88 (94)

CIRCULAR HEAD OF PORPHYRY, probably intended for setting in wood or plaster. It perhaps is, however, an unfinished piece.
Mexico. Width, 3 9/16 in. Pl. LVII, *bottom right.*

89

JADEITE DISK showing the head of an eagle.
Mexico. Diam. 5 1/16 in. Pl. LVII, *top right.*

90

JADEITE PLAQUE engraved with a conventionalized face of the Rain god Tlaloc.
Mexico. Height, 3 19/32 in. Pl. LVII, *top left.*

91

PAIR OF JADEITE DISKS. From the nature of the drilling it has been suggested that they once were the eyes of a wooden idol.
Mexico. Diam., 4⅝ in. Pl. LVII, *bottom left.*

92 (51, 52)

TWO SPIRALLY GROOVED TUBULAR BEADS of diopside-jadeite. They may have been the handles of fans used for the ceremonial lighting of fire.
State of Michoacan (?), Mexico. Lengths, 5 and 3¾ in.
Pl. LVIII, *bottom center.*

93 (34)

PLAQUE OF DIOPSIDE-JADEITE AND FELDSPAR. It displays a standing human figure with an elaborate headdress. A second head in profile appears at the left.
Mexico. Zapotec style (?). Height, 3½ in. Pl. LVIII, *top left.*

94 (36)

PENDANT OF PREHNITE. Like no. 93, it displays a standing figure with an elaborate headdress and again there is a head in profile projecting to the left. The subject in each case seems to be the same, but one is largely incised and the other is in fairly high relief. They may reflect the varying skills of different lapidaries or perhaps a chronological development in style.
State of Oaxaca, Mexico. Zapotec style (?). Height, 4 in.
Pl. LVIII, *bottom left.*

95

PLAQUE OF JADEITE. This shows the head and torso of a man with the hands upraised over the chest. The depth of the carving is intermediate between nos. 93 and 94.
Mexico. Zapotec style (?). Height, 4½ in.
Pl. LVIII, *top right.*

96 (30)

SMALL SEATED FIGURE OF DIOPSIDE-JADEITE.
Mexico. Mixtec style. Height, 2¾ in. Pl. LVIII, *bottom right.*

97 (90)

NECKLACE of twenty-two beaded gold disks with three tiny bells pendant from each. Each piece was modelled in wax, enclosed in a mold and cast separately. Several comparable necklaces were discovered at Monte Alban in the State of Oaxaca in the justly famous Tomb 7.
Where this necklace was found is not known. Half of it was acquired for the collection at a London auction; the other half turned up in New York several years later.
Mexico. Mixtec style ca. A.D. 1500. Each bead is 1 3/16 in. long and 3/16 in. thick. Pl. LIX.

98 (91)

PAIR OF GOLD EAR DISKS, found with no. 97. Each disk is surmounted by a humming-bird head shown in great detail. Body, wings and tail are suggested by wires. The whole was modelled in wax and cast in a single flow of metal. From each beak there hangs a plaque, representing perhaps a butterfly, which supports three small bells. The disks originally must have been mounted on a wooden base which was inserted in the ear.
Mexico. Mixtec style ca. A.D. 1500. *Length,* 2½ *in.* Pl. LIX, *center and bottom.*

99

WOODEN MASK COVERED WITH MOSAIC. The wood is very light, probably cedar. The mosaic is of turquoise, mother-of-pearl and pink shell. The two dark circles on the temples probably are tortoise shell.

In part the mosaic was set haphazardly, but it was laid in precise lines with each small piece cut to fit its individual place around the edges, around the eyes and the mouth, at the base and along the bridge of the nose, etc. The mouth with large canine teeth indicates that the face is only partly human and also represents an animal such as a jaguar. The large inlays, e.g., over one eye, on one cheek and on the nose, represent warts, which are rendered in relief on other specimens.

Turquoise mosaics were manufactured by our Pueblo Indians and in Peru, but they did not attain the high level of skill developed in Mexico by the Toltec and continued by the Aztec. The Mexican mosaics greatly aroused the admiration of the Spaniards, and, although they destroyed the major examples, such as the great idols, they shipped home many smaller pieces, including helmets, shields, masks, skulls, knife handles, etc. Of these, twenty-three, many of them fragmentary, exist today in six European museums.

Mosaic specimens have been encountered in archaeological excavations, but rarely under such circumstances that they could be restored. Others have been discovered in dry caves where they must have been hidden centuries ago to prevent their falling into Spanish hands as well as to continue the performance of pagan ceremonies forbidden by the Conquerors. The piece here illustrated belongs in this category and is, we believe, the nineteenth to be published.
Vicinity of Tilantongo, State of Oaxaca, Mexico. Mixtec culture. Height, 6⅛ *in.* Pl. LX.

100

CRUDELY BUT VIGOROUSLY CARVED JAGUAR of sericite. This is a soft stone, easy to work, usually employed by the poor for minor ornaments and beads. The legs are extended forward and back in the position known as the 'flying gallop'.
San Luis La Loma, Guerrero, Mexico. Length, 8 3/16 *in.* Pl. LXI, *top.*

101 (136)

EFFIGY JAR representing a hunter carrying home a deer. *State of Colima (?), Mexico. Tarascan style. Height,* 7 3/16 *in.* Pl. LXI, *bottom.*

THE MAYA AREA

See p. 24

102

STONE HEAD from the façade of Temple 26 at Copan. One of the most astounding architectural constructions in the New World, before its destruction by a landslide, was the Hieroglyphic Stairway which ascended Mound 26 at Copan. The vertical height was about 90 feet and the slope was 125, with five great statues set at regular intervals in the center. The width of the stairs was over 26 feet, and it was flanked by decorated balustrades which increased the total width to 33 feet (fig. 16).

Every vertical face of every step from top to bottom was carved with approximately 2,500 hieroglyphs, by far the longest single text produced by the Maya. Today there remain in order only two sections of text, each consisting of fifteen steps, but the stair has been partially restored. There are many dates in the text, most of them astronomical, but two which correspond to A.D. 711 and 756 probably represent the beginning and end of construction.

At the top of the Hieroglyphic Stairway stood Temple 26. It has completely disintegrated and not even foundation stones remain. Copan is unusual among Maya cities because little mortar was used in buildings except in the floors. Walls consisted of a clay and rubble heart encased in a heavy veneer of cut stone. Façades were adorned by carvings in the three-quarters round attached to the walls by long tenons.

The head here illustrated could only have come from the front of Temple 26, for, after falling over 100 feet, it was dug out of the debris at the base of the Hieroglyphic Stairway. The headdress and the nose (which has been restored) were damaged in the fall. It probably represents the Maize god, and it typifies the Maya concept of youthful beauty with soft contours and artificially flattened forehead.
Mound 26, Copan, Honduras. Classic Maya style. Height, 27½ *in.* Pl. LXII and fig. 16.

Fig. 16. *Hieroglyphic stairway leading to Temple 26 at Copan, Honduras.* Restoration by Tatiana Proskouriakoff.
Courtesy Carnegie Institution of Washington. (Cf. Cat. No. 102.)

103

PAINTED STUCCO HEAD. Copan at the eastern border of the Maya area is famous for its sculpture in stone; near the Northwestern frontier, notably at Palenque, most high-relief figures are of stucco, and stone carvings occur chiefly in low relief on large flat slabs.

The head here illustrated is again typical of the Maya ideal of beauty with flattened forehead and prominent nose and lips.

State of Campeche (?), Mexico. Classic Maya style. Height, $4\frac{7}{8}$ in. Pl. LXIII.

104

PAIR OF SHELL BAS-RELIEFS each representing a personage seated cross-legged on a low throne. Each has inlays of jade, those which have fallen out having been replaced with wax. In each case there is a band of glyphs running across the front of the throne. Both figures are shown with the head in profile looking over the shoulder, but the body and crossed legs are seen from the front. One arm hangs loosely at the side and the other is bent across the body. This asymmetrical pose is typical of the Late Classic style.

The lower right specimen in Pl. LXIV is the better preserved of the two. Incised glyphs, details of the legs and kilts, hands and headdress can be seen. Ear ornaments, necklace and wrist decoration were small cabochon-cut inlays of jade. The lower left example had twice as many jade insets, and most of the area of the skirt or kilt has been slightly countersunk. This may have been filled with a mosaic incrustation such as appears in Pl. LX.

Found with three others in a jar together with the objects in Pls. LXIX, LXX, LXXIII, LXXIV, LXXV. *State of Campeche, Mexico. Late Classic Maya style. Height, ca. 4 in. Pl. LXIV, bottom.*

104-A

PENDANT representing a human figure in profile. This belongs to the group known as 'Diving gods'. The body runs upward behind the face, and the doubled-over legs appear on top of the head with the feet projecting over the forehead. Another example, in Classic Veracruz style, appears in Pl. XV.

Late Classic Maya? Guatemala. Actual size. Pl. LXIV, top right.

104-B

PENDANT representing a face. The mouth, cut by string sawing, is one of the few known examples of this technique from Guatemala.

Late Classic Maya? Guatemala. Actual size. Pl. LXIV, top left.

105 (26)

JADEITE PENDANT representing a human head surmounted by a plumed headdress.

Late Classic Maya. Mexico. Height, $1\frac{7}{8}$ in. Pl. LXV, top left.

106 (23)

JADEITE PENDANT representing a human face and headdress. As in the previous specimen, the ear disks are linked by a cord under the chin.

Late Classic Maya. Mexico. Height, ca. $2\frac{1}{4}$ in. Pl. LXV, top center.

107 (22)

JADEITE PENDANT representing small profile human head in the open jaws of a serpent.

Mexico. Height, $1\frac{7}{16}$ in. Pl. LXV, top right.

108

SMALL JADEITE PENDANT showing an animal head in profile.

Mexico. Length, $\frac{3}{4}$ in. Pl. LXV, second row, center.

109 (27)

JADEITE PENDANT representing a human head.

Mexico. Width, $1\frac{1}{2}$ in. Pl. LXV, second row, left.

110 (20)

JADEITE PENDANT representing the head of Kinich Ahau, the Sun god.

Classic Maya. Mexico. Height, $1\frac{5}{8}$ in. Pl. LXV, second row, right.

111

SMALL JADEITE 'MASK' representing a monkey.

Highland Guatemala (?). Height, $1\frac{1}{8}$ in. Pl. LXV, third row, left.

112

JADEITE PENDANT showing a human face surrounded by scrolls.

Late Classic Maya. Mexico. Height, $2\frac{1}{4}$ in. Pl. LXV, third row, center.

113 (21)

JADEITE HEAD OF A MAN with a moustache and beard.

Mexico. Height, $1\frac{5}{8}$ in. Pl. LXV, bottom left.

114

HUMAN HEAD OF JADEITE shown in profile.

Mexico. Height, ca. $1\frac{1}{2}$ in. Pl. LXV, bottom center.

115, 116 (49, 50)

JADEITE 'BUTTONS' of unknown use. Similar pieces have been found in Southern Mexico and the Maya area. Diams., $1\frac{1}{16}$, $1\frac{3}{4}$ in. Pl. LXV, *third row, right*, and *bottom right*.

116-A

MASK OF MUSCOVITE (FUCHSITE). This mask is of a type differing from all others in this volume. The expression of the face speaks for itself. The thick lips and nostrils are in contrast with the relatively small eyes.

Pairs of small holes appear on the forehead, chin and below the eyes, presumably for the attachment of ornaments. To drill such small holes through the entire thickness of the stone would be a difficult task. Therefore a massive drill was applied to the back until there was only a thin skin to be pierced by the small drill. The break beside the nose was a mistake, caused by drilling too far with a large drill.

Mexico. Height, $5\frac{1}{4}$ in. Pl. LXVI, *top*.

The following objects, numbers 116-B–116-Q inclusive, are all of jadeite and come from the highlands of northwestern Guatemala; the workmanship is probably Late Classic or Post-Classic Maya.

116-B

PAIR OF EAR DISKS. The stems at the back have a small lateral hole. Diam., $1\frac{5}{8}$ in. Pl. LXVI, *top*.

116-C

SET OF FIFTY-EIGHT SMALL EAR DISKS. Although the stems are very short, each has a small hole drilled from the side. Why such a great number were manufactured is not clear. They may have been used as sequins. Diams., $\frac{3}{8}$ – $\frac{3}{4}$ in. Pl. LXVI, *bottom*.

116-D

EAR ORNAMENT with a hole for a shaft and three small holes for danglers.
Diam., 2 in. Pl. LXVII, *fourth, right center*.

116-E

EAR ORNAMENT, perhaps representing a flower.
Diam., $1\frac{5}{8}$ in. Pl. LXVII, *fourth, left center*.

116-F

BAR PENDANT decorated with a face and guilloche.
Length, $3\frac{3}{8}$ in. Pl. LXVII, *top right*.

116-G

PENDANT representing a standing human figure.
Height, 2 in. Pl. LXVII, *top left*.

116-H

PENDANT representing a human figure in profile.
Height, $3\frac{1}{4}$ in. Pl. LXVII, *top center*.

116-I

PENDANT terminating in an animal head (right) and a clasped fist (left). For a comparable Peruvian specimen, see Pl. CXXII, *bottom right*.
Length, $2\frac{1}{4}$ in. Pl. LXVII, *second right*.

116-J

PENDANT representing a human figure.
Height, $1\frac{1}{8}$ in. Pl. LXVII, *second left*.

116-K

PENDANT representing a human figure.
Height, $1\frac{1}{2}$ in. Pl. LXVII, *second, left center*.

116-L

PENDANT representing a bird head (vulture?).
Length, $2\frac{1}{8}$ in. Pl. LXVII, *third, right center*.

116-M

NECKLACE of twenty-one beads.
Length, ca. 18 in. Pl. LXVII, *bottom*.

116-N

PENDANT representing a human head in profile.
Height, 2 in. Pl. LXVII, *third, left center*.

116-O

PENDANT representing a crouching animal.
Length, $1\frac{3}{4}$ in. Pl. LXVII, *fifth, right center*.

116-P

RECTANGULAR BEAD.
Length, $2\frac{5}{8}$ in. Pl. LXVII, *sixth, right center*.

116-Q

TUBULAR BEAD.
Length, $1\frac{3}{8}$ in. Pl. LXVII, *seventh, right center*.

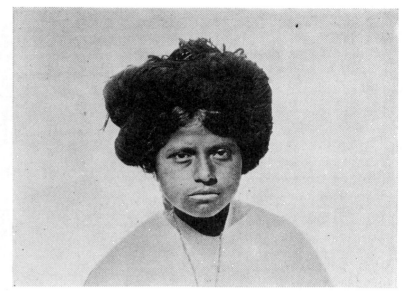

Fig. 17. *Side and back views of Maya figurine* illustrated in Pl. LXIX. (Cat. No. 119.)
Upper right: modern headdress, Isthmus of Tehuantepec, Mexico. Courtesy American Museum of Natural History.

117

JADE PLAQUE with two elaborate glyphs in a cartouche. This curious piece evidently fell into alien hands in ancient times, for someone started to recut it into a figurine with the glyphs upside down. The hole at the top and the cut above it are partly formed legs. The deep notches in the side are the beginning of shoulders, and two partly drilled eyes appear on the lower glyph.
Early Classic Maya. State of Campeche. Mexico. Height, ca. 4 in. Pl. LXVIII, top.

118

JADEITE PLAQUE carved in relief. A cross-legged personage, perhaps the Maize god, is seated in a niche. He wears an elaborate plumed headdress, ear studs (Pl. LVI, *bottom*), a bar pendant on his chest (Pl. LV, *bottom*), wristlets and anklets consisting in part of tubular beads laced parallel to each other. The body is shown full-face, but the head is turned over the left shoulder. The left arm is extended and two small pellets can be seen dropping from the hand.

The plaque probably symbolizes the ceremonial sowing of maize, the staple crop of the Maya. Outside the niche on the right there is a profile head of Kinich Ahau, the Maya Sun god, who also is portrayed in Pl. LXV, *second row, right*. Below the niche is a profile head of a very conventionalized serpent with the open jaws facing to the right. This is a symbolic earth monster upon which the grains of maize are falling.

Originally the plaque was light blue, but it has been stained brown by iron rust, probably because it was buried with a mirror of iron pyrites.

The style is very Late Classic Maya. Numerous details in the carving correspond to stylistic variations seen on stelae dated 10.1.0.0.0 in the Maya count (=A.D. 827). Many of these traits occur at the ruins of Seibal in the upper Usumacinta valley. This specimen, however, may have come from the vicinity of Nebaj in the highlands of Guatemala, where several similar pieces have been found. The finest Maya jades passed in trade or as tribute over great distances, and there is positive evidence that some were inherited for many generations before they were buried with their owners.

Late Classic Maya. Nebaj, Guatemala. Height, ca. 5¼ in. Pl. LXVIII, *bottom*.

119

SOLID POTTERY STATUETTE representing a standing man with upraised arms, perhaps an orator. The position of the hands suggests someone trying to quiet a tumultuous gathering. The massive body and bald head imply that he is far from young.

Dress consists of a narrow apron which hangs from a belt and reaches the ground. Also he wears a knee-length jacket, open in front. There are three semi-circular holes in both sides, each with flaps sticking out. The headdress consists of spikes, the nature of which is not clear, surmounted by a series of loops. These probably represent hair, real or false, for such headdresses are still to be seen in south Mexico and Guatemala (fig. 17). Chin and cheeks are concealed by a wing-shaped device, seemingly of flexible material, somewhat like the so-called mouth masks found in Peru.

Three tiny beads appear on the brow ridge above the nose. This was a method for making the individual cross-eyed, which the Maya, at least until the sixteenth century, considered a mark of beauty. The large beads in the necklace probably were of jade. They support a shell below which hang tubular beads.

State of Campeche, Mexico (see no. 132). *Classic Maya, Jaina style.* Height, 8¾ in. Pl. LXIX, and fig. 17.

120

SOLID POTTERY FIGURINE representing a seated individual of high rank. He wears a narrow fringed apron, a short kilt and a shawl reaching to the waist, beneath which his arms are crossed. On either shoulder there are large disks joined by a cord which is loosely looped around the neck. The headdress consists of a voluminous turban to which are attached three more disks and short upright plumes. A necklace of spherical beads and ear ornaments complete the costume.

State of Campeche, Mexico (see no. 132). *Classic Maya, Jaina style.* Height, ca. 6⅛ in. Pl. LXX.

121

SOLID POTTERY FIGURINE representing a standing warrior with a circular shield. The right arm is held up in front of the face in what may be a gesture of peace or perhaps merely to shield the eyes from the sun. A snake encircles the left forearm. Over the nose is a small device for causing cross eyes.

The headdress of this specimen, a side view of which appears in fig. 18, is most unusual, and we cannot state

Fig. 18. *Side view of Maya figurine illustrated in Pl. LXXI, left.* (Cat. No. 121.)

of what materials it was made. The necklace also is of uncommon type.

State of Campeche, Mexico (see no. 132). *Late Classic Maya, Jaina style.* Height, ca. 12¾ in. Pl. LXXI, *left*, and fig. 18.

122 (135)

HOLLOW POTTERY FIGURINE AND WHISTLE representing a seated woman clad in a long dress. The face apparently was modelled by hand, but the body was cast in a mold. Flattened forehead and a device to cause cross eyes in the center are typical Maya features. Scarification or tattooing appears around the mouth. She wears a two-strand choker around the neck with an elaborate knot at the back.

Jonuta style. Mexico. Late Classic Maya. Height, 6¾ in. Pl. LXXI, *right*, and fig. 19.

Fig. 20. *Detail of Maya figurine illustrated in* Pl. LXXII. *left.* (Cat. No. 123.)

123 (132)

PARTLY HOLLOW POTTERY FIGURINE representing a standing bearded man with folded arms. Only the body is hollow and there is the mouthpiece of a whistle behind the right shoulder. He wears a short kilt with a pouch in front, a necklace, ear plugs and a huge headdress.

The headdress consists of a skull cap with small elements dangling over the nose (to cause cross eyes) and on the forehead above each eye. Above there is a row of vertical irregular tubes. These we take to be the leg bones of jaguar with the ends cut off, which were employed in Central and South America to extract disease by suction. If this identification is correct, the figure represents a shaman or witch doctor with his paraphernalia worn around his head and carried in a purse. The top of the headdress is a series of coils recalling those in Pl. LXIX and fig. 17.

State of Campeche, Mexico. Classic Maya, Jaina style. Height, 8¾ in. Pl. LXXII, *left*, and fig. 20.

124 (134)

HOLLOW MOLDED POTTERY FIGURE representing a standing woman (?) holding a blue plate. She wears an apron and a skirt from the waist to the ankles. The wrists are adorned with cuffs. There is a necklace of graduated beads with a pendant of two elements, one of which may

Fig. 19. *Side view of Maya figurine illustrated in* Pl. LXXI, *right.* (Cat. No. 122.)

be a shell. The headdress represents a bird (vulture?) in profile with white wings and tail at the left and at the right a head and beak holding a tasseled rosette. This piece is hollow and rattles.

Island of Jaina, Mexico. Classic Maya. Height, 5 9/16 in. Pl. LXXII, *right.*

125

SOLID POTTERY FIGURE representing a standing man who holds a shield. The right hand is open as if to grasp a spear or spear-thrower (Pl. XLIX). Garments consist of a short apron, a scalloped blue kilt and a yellow jacket, open at the front and fringed, perhaps with shells.

The hair is in braids which have been cut off square just below the shoulders. Globular beads around the neck support a large shell on the breast. The headdress consists of spikes (as in Pl. LXIX) and is surmounted by an animal head, perhaps a dog. Guaymí Indians still wear stuffed animals for ceremonial adornment. The shield probably represents Mexican influence, for shields with a similar pattern were used by the Aztec and pictured in their codices.

State of Campeche, Mexico (see no. 132). *Late Classic Maya, Jaina style.* Height, 8 in. Pl. LXXIII.

126

HOLLOW POTTERY FIGURE which is also a whistle. The mouthpiece is under the left knee. It represents a seated, cross-legged individual who holds a concave oval object in the right hand. The features are strongly modelled and the chin is tattooed.

He wears the usual belt, apron and kilt as well as a short cloak, open in the front, with four rows of spikes on the sides and back. Similar spikes also occur in this and other headdresses (Pls. LXIX, LXXIII) but, although evidently in common use, we have not been able to ascertain their nature. Other elements in the headdress include a cowl, flaps and a tall projecting spine at the top. The necklace is of globular beads with a tubular bead in the center.

State of Campeche, Mexico (see no. 132). *Classic Maya, Jaina style.* Height, 8 1/8 in. Pl. LXXIV.

127

HOLLOW POTTERY FIGURINE representing an old man embracing a young girl. Few phallic symbols or scenes of love-making have been found in the New World outside the Mochica area in Peru. The man in this specimen evidently is old as attested by his shrunken face and bald head (fig. 21). Evidently he is a person of importance, for

Fig. 21. *Maya figurine illustrated in Pl. LXXV. (Cat. No. 127.)*

he wears a huge headdress consisting of a deer's head set on some folded material, perhaps leather.

The girl evidently is young and typifies the Classic Maya concept of beauty with flattened forehead, large nose and soft facial contours. Small beads for causing cross eyes hang above her nose. She wears a headdress of tall loops, similar to but less elaborate than those seen on male figurines. Around the neck is a scarf, knotted at the back as on the female figure in Fig. 19.

State of Campeche, Mexico (see no. 132). *Classic Maya, Jaina style.* Height, 10 1/16 in. Pl. LXXV and fig. 21.

128 (133)

SOLID POTTERY FIGURINE representing a seated cross-legged man. He is adorned with an elaborate headdress the top of which is missing, a necklace of graduated beads with a face on the central bead, ear plugs and mosaic cuffs. A robe covers him from chest to ankles. Teeth are shown in fine detail.

Island of Jaina, Mexico. Classic Maya. Height, 5⅜ in. Pl. LXXVIII, center.

129

POTTERY FIGURINE representing a woman seated cross-legged. A long robe covers her from neck to ankle except the wrists and hands. The unusual headdress consists of a solid base terraced to frame the face. Above is a huge hat with zigzag edges. The original probably was of straw, for hats with very broad brims are woven in Yucatan today.

State of Campeche, Mexico. Classic Maya, Jaina style. Height, 5 13/16 in. Pl. LXXVIII, left.

130

SOLID POTTERY FIGURINE representing a standard bearer. This specimen is unusual in several ways. For one thing, the individual is relatively simply dressed and adorned. His headdress, to be sure, has loops at the top but less elaborate than those on other male figurines. His necklace is a shell on a string. Furthermore, the round standard, perhaps a shield, was made separately and the shaft supporting it is modern. A feature not seen in other specimens is the circular base to which the feet are luted, perhaps an afterthought made necessary to balance the weight of the shield.

State of Campeche, Mexico. Classic Maya, Jaina style. Height, 7 1/16 in. (with standard, 11⅛ in.). Pl. LXXVIII, right.

131

LARGE POTTERY FIGURINE-WHISTLE which represents an individual seated cross-legged. As in Pl. LXXIV, clothing consists of a cape and skirt reaching to the ankles. This personage may be identified as male, however, by the shortcut hair and masculine type of cuffs.

There are several unusual features. In the first place, all exposed flesh – face and neck, arms and feet – seems to have been painted in a light tone of blue-green which is definitely a different pigment from the dark blue on the headdress and clothing. Blue was a sacred color to the Mayas, and victims destined to human sacrifice were smeared with it, as well as the sacrificial stone. Except for the skin color, there is no other suggestion that the figurine represents a captive prepared for this rite. The color more probably signifies ceremonies held during the month *Yaxkin*, when the Maya covered with blue 'all the appliances of all their pursuits, from the priests to the spindles of the women'.

The enormous headdress consists of three principal elements which suggest stuffed bags. They are held in place by ordinary ropes and by lashings covered with small projecting nodules, the nature of which we cannot identify. In addition there are three rosettes. At the back, the hair hangs below the headdress in two layers, each of which have been cut in a straight line across the base of the neck.

On the brow ridge over the nose, the customary small bead is displayed. The chin and bridge of the nose are adorned with small dots which must represent tattooing or scarification. In addition, both the upper and lower lips have been cut so that they give the effect of a beaded edge. This mutilation probably represents the offering of one's own blood to the gods, which also was done by piercing the ear or tongue. See no. 6.

As in the case of no. 126, there is a whistle in the base of the left hip.

Late Classic Maya. Style of Jonuta. State of Campeche, Mexico. Height, 16½ in. Pls. LXXVI, LXXVII.

132

SHALLOW POLYCHROME BOWL with short tripod legs. The legs each have a lateral vent to permit the passage of air during firing. The inner rim carries a pair of complex conventionalized patterns. On the floor a bird, perhaps a vulture, is shown with glyph-like elements attached to the head and chest.

This bowl had been inverted over the mouth of a large jar to protect the objects stored inside. These included *inter alia* the specimens in this volume illustrated in Pls. LXIV, *bottom*, LXIX, LXX, LXXI, *left*, LXXIII, LXXIV, LXXV. Other such caches have occasionally been found in Maya ruins as foundation offerings for stelae and temples or in tombs.

State of Campeche, Mexico. Late Classic Maya. Diam., 12¾ in. Pl. LXXIX.

133

POLYCHROME JAR. At the top is a band of glyphs functional rather than decorative, for, as seen in fig. 22, no two are alike. The principal decoration, repeated on each side, consists of a picture of the shell god, identified technically as god N. This was the Maya deity who ruled

Fig. 22. *Glyph band on Maya polychrome jar* illustrated in Pl. LXXXII, *top*. (Cat. No. 133.)

over the five unlucky inter-calendary days at the end of the year. Part of the glyph over his head in Pl. LXXXII, *top*, and at the bottom left in fig. 22, apparently represents a shell and the whole glyph may record his name. He is usually portrayed as an old man.

A shell deity was worshipped throughout the Maya area from Classic times until the Conquest. He is also represented in Mexican codices. In Peru during the Mochica period, a shell god with a jaguar head is found both in painted and modelled pottery.

State of Yucatan, Mexico. Classic Maya. Height, ca. 6⅜ in. Pl. LXXXII, *top*, and fig. 22.

134

POLYCHROME CYLINDRICAL JAR. The shape is typical of Late Classic Maya, but the decoration is unusual both in concept and execution. The colors, orange and brown, were evidently applied very wet, for in places they have run together.

The design may be described basically as two large orange disks on opposite sides of the vessel, linked by rows of smaller orange disks, everything then being enclosed by brown borders. The smaller disks all are divided in half by the so-called negative painting technique, a process akin to batik in which the areas not to be colored were protected by wax until the painting was finished. In this case the wax was applied first, then the orange, lastly the brown, after which the wax was removed.

Negative painting, both by itself and in combination with direct painting, is found in both continents of the New World, but neither is common in the Maya area.

State of Yucatan (?), Mexico. Late Classic Maya. Height, 7⁹⁄₁₆ in. Pl. LXXX, *left*.

135 (137)

POLYCHROME MAYA JAR. There are two inter-related scenes, shown in Pl. LXXXI, both involving a ceremony connected with a deer. At the left, there is a conventionalized tree sprouting from a human head symbolizing the earth. A serpent is coiled around the trunk and there are two human figures on branches on opposite sides of the tree. Beneath the tree are a pair of deer seated as if they were human or perhaps men disguised as deer. To the right of the tree is a standing attendant who holds a bunch of bamboo spears in one hand and blows a large conch-shell trumpet.

In the right-hand scene, there is a large deer guarded by two identically dressed men with spears. One blows a large shell trumpet. The other apparently is tearing out the antlers. Above is a bird, probably a vulture. The deer wears a blanket covered with death symbols consisting of cross-bones.

On the actual vessel these two scenes must be viewed separately but they evidently were considered a unit. All the men portrayed are adorned with cross-hatched circles painted on their bodies, corresponding to the body marks on the tree serpent. Several have individual glyphs beside them which probably record their names.

In front of the deer's chest there are two numerical glyphs, presumably attached to a day and month sign. A tentative reading might be the day 8 Ahau and the month 13.(?)

This specimen once was in the collection of Enrique Cámara of Mérida, Yucatan.

Classic Maya. Height, 7⅜ in. Pls. LXXX, *right*, and LXXXI.

136

POLISHED ORANGE-WARE BOWL. This vessel is decorated by a fluted cornice and three incised bands. Two of these, at the top and bottom, are guilloches. The third consists of elongated step frets, partly outlined by cross-hatching.

State of Yucatan, Mexico. Tula-Toltec period. Height, ca. 4⅜ in. Pl. LXXXIII, *top*.

137

CARVED SLATE-WARE BOWL. The decoration consists of two grotesque figures seated in the open jaws of very much conventionalized plumed serpents. Each holds a staff in front of the body and they face each other. The feathered bodies of the snakes undulate to the opposite side of the jar where the tails merge (Pl. LXXXIII, *bottom*). On the rim there are cartouches containing conventionalized serpent heads.

State of Yucatan, Mexico. Late Classic Maya. Height, 4³⁄₁₆ in. Pls. LXXXIII, *bottom*, LXXXIV.

138

HEMISPHERICAL BOWL of light-brown clay. Originally there were three sunken oval panels with carved bas-reliefs, but one has been destroyed. These were separated by incised columns of glyphs. Each oval panel had a shorter column of glyphs. None of the glyphs can be deciphered and it therefore is uncertain whether they form a single text or several.

The two surviving reliefs are shown in Pl. LXXXV. The lower one portrays a man seated on a low dais. He points at a pottery jar. The striped oval objects in front of him probably represent cacao pods. His curious headdress perhaps represents the branches of a cacao tree before harvesting.

From Mexico to Panama, cacao beans were the standard currency in aboriginal times. This made possible the trade which flourished throughout the entire region. The possession of lands where cacao orchards abounded made their owners rich. After the Spanish conquest, cacao continued in use as currency, in some places until the middle nineteenth century when the exchange rate was twenty beans for two candles or a *real*. In the early sixteenth century, however, a hundred beans would buy a slave.

The other panel in Pl. LXXXV, *top*, shows a man sprawling in an awkward position across a dais while a bird, perhaps a heron, plucks at his headdress. A single cacao pod appears under his elbow and beyond are what appear to be two rectangular containers.

State of Yucatan, Mexico. Classic Maya. Diam., 6⅜ in. Pl. LXXXV.

139

CYLINDRICAL SLATE-WARE JAR. The principal panel portrays a chief seated cross-legged on a throne. Legs and body are seen from in front, but the head is in profile. He is adorned with wristlets, a broad collar and a huge headdress. He faces a panel shaped like an inverted **T** which contains five glyphs. On the opposite side of the vessel there is a diagonal panel in which the same glyph is repeated five times.

State of Yucatan, Mexico. Late Classic Maya. Height, 6 7/16 in. Pl. LXXXII, bottom.

140

ONYX MARBLE BOWL. This unusual specimen was the work of a master craftsman. It displays an incised text of hieroglyphs encircling the outer rim. Below, in three panels, are three seated figures, each holding religious symbols, two of them accompanied by additional texts. Each incised panel is separated from the next by six flutes. As the lip is only an eighth of an inch wide, the walls of the vessel can scarcely measure half of that at the inner curve of the flutes. The incised lines had been filled with a dark pigment.

The figure seen in Pl. LXXXVI, *top*, evidently outranks the other two as he is larger, and occupies more vertical space although leaning forward. He is seated cross-legged in a very conventionalized serpent's jaws. Face and legs are shown in profile, but the body is so twisted that both arms and shoulders appear from the front. The wall of the jar has been cut back in front of the face so that it stands out in low relief. The headdress is relatively simple for a Maya dignitary but the ear ornaments are elaborate. The necklace is of globular beads but the wristlets and belt are of tubular beads, strung parallel. A long tasselled loin-cloth extends beyond the knees.

In the hands, extended as if in the act of presentation, there is a ceremonial bar representing the two-headed monster which to the Maya symbolized the earth. Among the Aztec this monster was conceived as a huge crocodile floating in a vast ocean. The right head on the jar, with

Fig. 23. *Three Maya figures from the incised onyx marble bowl illustrated in Pls. LXXXVI and LXXXVII. (Cat. No. 140.)*

upturned snout, is definitely saurian. The other head has a long curling nose, fangs, but no lower jaw. It is surmounted by a so-called Kan cross with shell and leaf symbols on top. At the extreme left are two dots and a bar, representing 1+1+5, i.e., 7.

The word *Kan*, which is one of the Maya day-names, literally means 'precious'. The Kan cross symbolizes blue, water, turquoise and ripe maize. It is often shown on the forehead of the Earth Monster combined with 7. In Mixtec codices of later date, individuals are frequently given a numerical day-name, as if we were named for our birthdays. We may interpret the entire ceremonial bar as 'Precious Lord Seven Earth'.

The next panel to the right (Pl. LXXXVI, *bottom*) again contains a cross-legged figure with the head only in profile. He apparently wears a skirt as creases are shown on the legs. The left arm is extended across the body and holds in the hand a crocodile head similar to the right-hand head of the Earth Monster in the first panel. This head, however, is shown mouth up. A latticed band across the face and top of the head may represent mosaic inlay.

Above is the monkey-like head of the North Star god, to which is attached the number 7. On the opposite side of the panel are three glyphs referring to the day Imix, the North Star god and the north.

The third panel (Pl. LXXXVII, *top*) contains the smallest of the three figures, also seated cross-legged with head only in profile. Presumably the least important in rank, he is the most elaborately dressed, for he wears a head-dress with long plumes, ear and wrist ornaments, a poncho with decorated borders, and, on the chest, both a mosaic gorget and a necklace of round beads.

This individual carries in his right hand a head with a long curling nose and no lower jaw, corresponding to the left-hand head in the first panel except that the Kan cross is eliminated and the number is four dots and a bar or 9 (1+1+1+1+5=9). It seems probable that the association of different numbers with the same divinity represents different aspects or functions.

Taken as a whole, this vessel portrays the ceremonial offering of religious symbols, representing the earth, probably to the North Star god on a certain day, Imix.

The inscription on the rim, unlike most pottery vessels, is functional and refers both to Imix and the North Star god. There is also a distance number, 4820 (13 tuns of 360 days each plus 7 uinals of 20 days each) leading to (or from) the day 4 Ahau.

This is the day on which all Katuns (ca. 20-year periods) ended. In this case we may have dates of 9.15.0.0.0 or 10.8.0.0.0, A.D. 731 or 987. Miss Tatiana Proskouriakoff and Mr. Eric Thompson of the Carnegie Institution of Washington agree that on stylistic grounds one is too early and the other too late. They believe that the day 4 Ahau may refer to a 5- or 10-year period.
State of Campeche, Mexico. Classic Maya. Diam., ca. 6¼ in. Pls. LXXXVI, LXXXVII and fig. 23.

141

ONYX MARBLE BOWL. This vessel is said to have been found with no. 140. It is fluted all the way around and the walls are very thin. The rim was plaster-coated and painted blue, a color regarded as sacred by the Maya. In preparing for human sacrifice both the victim and the stone on which he was executed were painted blue.
State of Campeche, Mexico. Classic Maya. Diam., ca. 6¾ in. Pl. LXXXVIII, *bottom*.

HONDURAS
See p. 29

142

MARBLE BOWL. The handles are birds' heads in high relief. Typical scroll patterns adorn the walls. This vessel originally stood on cylindrical tripod legs, but they have been broken off or ground down. Although the workmanship and material is typical of the Ulua Valley, this piece had passed in trade for a long distance, for it was discovered in Costa Rica. It once was in the Lines collection.
Nicoya peninsula, Costa Rica. Diam., ca. 8 1/16 in. Pl. LXXXVIII, *top*.

COSTA RICA
See p. 30

The objects in Pls. LXXXIX–XCI, XCIII, XCIV inclusive are all from the Nicoya peninsula in north-western Costa Rica.

143

DIORITE CLUB HEAD. Among the implements characteristic of the Nicoya peninsula are stone club heads with a large hole in the center for inserting a wooden shaft. They may be in the form of stone rings, either smooth or spiked or they may be carved to represent animals, birds or human heads. The example here illustrated may portray a jaguar head.
Nacascola, Nicoya peninsula. Length, 4 in. Pl. XC, *center*.

144

NECKLACE OF JADEITE.
Scale, 5/7. Pl. XC.

145

NECKLACE OF JADEITE.
Ca. actual size. Pl. LXXXIX.

146 (4)

AXE GOD OF JADEITE representing a man with an animal headdress.
Length, 8½ in. Pl. XCI, *bottom left.*

147 (6)

AXE GOD OF JADEITE representing a man.
Length, 5 in. Pl. XCI, *bottom center.*

148 (5)

AXE GOD OF JADEITE representing a man with a serpent tongue.
Length, 6¹³⁄₁₆ in. Pl. XCI, *bottom right.*

149

AXE GOD OF JADEITE representing a man.
Ca. actual size. Pl. LXXXIX, *center left.*

150

AXE GOD OF JADEITE representing a man.
Ca. ⅔. Pl. XCIII, *top right.*

151

AXE GOD OF JADEITE representing a man.
Ca. ⅔. Pl. XCIII, *second row.*

152

AXE GOD OF JADEITE representing a man.
Ca. ⅔. Pl. XCIII, *bottom left.*

153

AXE GOD OF JADEITE representing a man.
Ca. actual size. Pl. XCIV, *bottom, center left.*

154

AXE GOD OF JADEITE representing a bird.
Ca. actual size. Pl. LXXXIX, *center.*

155

PENDANT OF JADEITE representing a bird.
Ca. ⅔. Pl. XCIII, *top center.*

156

AXE GOD OF JADEITE representing a bird.
Ca. ⅔. Pl. XCIII, *top, center right.*

157

AXE GOD OF JADEITE representing a bird.
Ca. actual size. Pl. XCIV, *top left.*

158

AXE GOD OF JADEITE representing a bird.
Ca. actual size. Pl. XCIV, *bottom left.*

159

AXE GOD OF JADEITE representing a bird.
Ca. actual size. Pl. XCIV, *bottom right.*

160

AXE GOD OF JADEITE.
Ca. actual size. Pl. LXXXIX, *center right.*

161

AXE GOD OF JADEITE.
Ca. ⅔. Pl. XCIII, *top, center left.*

162

AXE GOD OF JADEITE.
Ca. ⅔. Pl. XCIII, *second row.*

163

AXE GOD OF JADEITE.
Ca. ⅔. Pl. XCIII, *second row.*

164

AXE GOD OF JADEITE.
Ca. ⅔. Pl. XCIII, *second row.*

165

PENDANT OF JADEITE.
Ca. actual size. Pl. XCIV, *top, center right.*

166

PENDANT OF JADEITE representing a bird.
Ca. actual size. Pl. LXXXIX, *below* Cat. No. 154.

167

PENDANT OF JADEITE representing a bird.
Ca. ⅔. Pl. XCIII, *second row, left.*

168

PENDANT OF JADEITE representing a bird.
Ca. ⅔. Pl. XCIII, *second row, right.*

169

PENDANT OF JADEITE representing a cebus monkey
with a bird head.
Actual size. Pl. LXXXIX, *below* Cat. No. 166.

170

PENDANT OF JADEITE representing a two-headed
crocodile.
Ca. ⅔. Pl. XCIII, *top left.*

171

PENDANT OF JADEITE representing a crocodile (?).
Ca. ⅔. Pl. XCIII, *bottom center.*

172

PENDANT OF JADEITE representing a man upside down.
Ca. ⅔. Pl. XCIII, *second row.*

173

PENDANT OF JASPER representing a woman.
Ca. actual size. Pl. XCIV, *bottom, center right.*

174

PENDANT OF JADEITE representing a double-headed
snake.
Ca. actual size. Pl. XCIV, *top, center left.*

175

PENDANT OF JASPER representing an animal.
Ca. actual size. Pl. XCIV, *second row, right.*

176

PENDANT OF JASPER representing a turtle.
Ca. actual size. Pl. XCIV, *third row, right.*

177 (16)

WINGED PENDANT OF JADEITE representing extended
wings of a bat.
For an explanation of this form, see no. 208. Length,
$4\frac{7}{16}$ in. Pl. XCI, *top left.*

178 (15)

WINGED PENDANT OF JADEITE representing the
extended wings of a bat.
See no. 208. Length, $3\frac{3}{4}$ in. Pl. XCI, *top right.*

179

PENDANT OF JADEITE.
Ca. actual size. Pl. LXXXIX, *top.*

180

PENDANT OF VOLCANIC TUFF.
Ca. actual size. Pl. LXXXIX, *bottom left.*

181

PENDANT OF JADEITE.
Ca. actual size. Pl. LXXXIX, *bottom right.*

182

PENDANT OF JADEITE.
Height, $2\frac{1}{2}$ in. Pl. XCI, *center.*

183

PENDANT OF JADEITE.
Ca. ⅔. Pl. XCIII, *bottom right.*

184

GLOBULAR PENDANT OF JASPER.
Ca. actual size. Pl. XCIV, *top right.*

185

PENDANT OF JADEITE.
Ca. actual size. Pl. XCIV, *second row, left.*

186

JADEITE BEADS carved in the shape of fish vertebrae.
Ca. actual size. Pl. XCIV, *third row, left.*

All objects in Pls. XCII, XCV, XCVI, inclusive are from the vicinity of Guápiles in northeastern Costa Rica.

187

NECKLACE OF JADEITE. The color is typical of Costa Rica.
Ca. ⅔. Pl. XCII, *top right.*

188, 189

TWO HUGE TUBULAR JADEITE BEADS. These and similar specimens from the same region represent the deepest drilling of jade found in aboriginal America. They were drilled from each end. Shafts up to eight inches deep have been observed. It is not known with certainty how these large beads were worn, but they may correspond to the gold bars used by women on the adjacent coast of Colombia to support their breasts.
Length, 10 15/16 in. each. Pl. XCII, *left.*

190

SMALL AXE GOD OF JADEITE.
Ca. ⅔. Pl. XCII, *bottom, center left.*

191, 192

TWO BEADS OF JADEITE. Both have been drilled lengthwise and a hole has then been drilled through one side wall.
Ca. ⅔. Pl. XCII, *bottom, center right.*

193

JADEITE PENDANT made by cutting a celt first in halves, then in quarters.
Ca. ⅔. Pl. XCII, *bottom right.*

194

JADEITE PENDANT representing a man. The holes for suspension are in the ears.
Ca. actual size. Pl. XCV, *center row, right.*

195

JADEITE PENDANT representing a man. This is an example of string sawing, a technique typical of the locality. To free the arms and legs, first a hole was drilled. Then a string impregnated with an abrasive was inserted and a slot, narrower than the hole, was cut by sawing.
Ca. actual size. Pl. XCV, *bottom center.*

196

JADEITE PENDANT portraying a greatly conventionalized human figure.
Ca. actual size. Pl. XCV, *bottom left.*

197, 198

A PAIR OF JADEITE PENDANTS representing crocodiles holding their tails and dancing on their hind legs. This concept apparently was developed in the Province of Coclé or the Asuero peninsula in Panama where it was rendered on polychrome dishes or repoussé gold disks.
Ca. actual size. Pl. XCV, *top center and right.*

199

JADEITE PENDANT in the shape of a crocodile.
Ca. actual size. Pl. XCV, *bottom right.*

200

JADEITE PENDANT representing a crested animal, perhaps an iguana.
Ca. actual size. Pl. XCV, *below No. 197.*

201

JADEITE PENDANT portraying a monkey with the tail curved over the head.
Ca. actual size. Pl. XCV, *top left.*

202

JADEITE PENDANT.
Ca. actual size. Pl. XCV, *center row, left.*

203

JADEITE PENDANT.
Ca. actual size. Pl. XCV, *center row, middle.*

204

JADEITE PENDANT representing a snake. This form could have been produced only by string sawing.
Scale, ¾. Pl. XCVI, *center left.*

205

JADEITE PENDANT representing a bird with exaggerated bill, cut by string sawing.
Scale, ¾. Pl. XCVI, *center right.*

206

JADEITE PENDANT consisting of a weird female figure surrounded by a stirrup-shape frame, all cut from one piece of jade. The head is a rectangular block with no other features than two pits for eyes. It is surmounted by a pair of animal heads in profile.
Scale, $\frac{3}{4}$. Pl. XCVI, *bottom left*.

207

JADEITE PENDANT. This piece is a simplification of the symbolism expressed in no. 206, obtained by elimination of the body, arms and legs. There remain the stirrup-like frame, the two eye pits and the pair of profile animal heads. Evidently these elements have some ceremonial significance by themselves which is lost to us today.
Scale, $\frac{3}{4}$. Pl. XCVI, *bottom right*.

208

JADEITE PENDANT in the form of a bat with outspread wings. So-called winged pendants have been found in Mexico (Pl. LIII, *bottom*), Costa Rica (Pl. XCI, *top left, right*), Panama (Pl. CIX, *top*), northern Colombia and Venezuela, and in the West Indies as far north as Puerto Rico. The usual form is a flattened oval or oblong which was suspended horizontally. The material may be jade, agate and other stones, or shell. Occasionally the body and head of a bat was carved in the center, indicating that the whole group symbolizes a bat with extended wings.
The example here illustrated, found near Guápiles, is perhaps the most complex yet recorded. The head with pointed ears and the short legs are typical of the bat. The wings, however, are elaborately carved to represent crocodile heads in profile. An almost equally intricate jade example has been found in the Nicoya peninsula.
Length, ca. $2\frac{3}{4}$ in. Pl. XCVI, *top*.

PANAMA

See p. 31

All objects in Pls. XCVII–CVII inclusive are of Veraguas style. Most of them are from the Province of Veraguas; a few are trade pieces found in the Province of Chiriquí. All come from graves.

209

MASSIVE EAGLE PENDANT of cast gold.
Width, $5\frac{3}{4}$ in. Pl. XCVII.

209-A

MASSIVE EAGLE PENDANT of cast gold.
Veraguas style. Panama. Width, $5\frac{1}{2}$ in. (not illustrated; see No. 209).

210

EAGLE PENDANT of cast gold.
Width, ca. $6\frac{5}{8}$ in. Pl. XCVIII, *top*.

211

EAGLE PENDANT of cast tumbaga with feet and wings of unusual type.
Width, $5\frac{1}{8}$ in. Pl. XCVIII, *bottom left*.

212

DOUBLE-HEADED EAGLE PENDANT of cast tumbaga. The protruding eyes are small bells, a characteristic of Veraguas metalwork.
Width, $4\frac{5}{8}$ in. Pl. XCVIII, *bottom right*.

213

EAGLE PENDANT of cast tumbaga. The head is flanked by crocodile heads in profile; crocodile scales are attached to the upper edge of the wings, which have small heads at their tips.
Width, ca. $4\frac{1}{2}$ in. Pl. XCIX, *top*.

214

CAST GOLD EAGLE PENDANT. The headdress is a symbol usually seen on the tongues of frogs (Pl. CIII, *bottom*).
Width, $4\frac{1}{8}$ in. Pl. XCIX, *bottom*.

215

MINIATURE CAST GOLD EAGLE PENDANT. The wing tips are profile bird heads upside down.
Height, $\frac{7}{8}$ in. Pl. CII, *second row, middle*.

216

MINIATURE CAST GOLD EAGLE PENDANT.
Height, $\frac{5}{8}$ in. Pl. CII, *second row, left*.

217 (61)

CAST GOLD PENDANT representing a double-headed bird. This is not an eagle.
Width, $2\frac{1}{2}$ in. Pl. CII, *bottom left*.

218

COMPOUND BIRD PENDANT OF CAST GOLD with three heads, three bodies, two wings and one tail.
Width, ca. 2½ in. Pl. CII, *bottom center.*

219

PENDANT OF CAST GOLD representing an unusual type of bird, perhaps a heron. The beak is long and there are plumes on the head. The eyes are bells.
Width, ca. 2 in. Pl. C, *center.*

220

GOLD PENDANT in the shape of a frog. Typically there are two tongues terminating in triangular serpent heads or spirals.
Length, 3 5/16 in. Pl. CIII, *bottom left.*

221

CAST GOLD PENDANT in the shape of a frog.
Length, 2 9/16 in. Pl. CIII, *bottom right.*

222

CAST GOLD PENDANT representing a frog.
Width, 2 5/8 in. Pl. CIV, *top left.*

223 (65)

CAST GOLD PENDANT representing a jaguar.
Length, 4½ in. Pl. CIII, *top left and right.*

224

CAST GOLD PENDANT with a jaguar head and body. The feet are profile crocodile heads, identified by the curling snouts. The twin tails have triangular serpent heads at the tip. This specimen and no. 225 emphasize the fact that Veraguas goldsmiths usually were not attempting to portray the forms of nature, but more or less monstrous mythological beings whose symbolism and magical powers are now forgotten.
Length, 2¾ in. Pl. CIV, *top, left center.*

225

CAST GOLD PENDANT representing a compound monster. The head appears to be that of a frog (Pl. CIII, *bottom left*) with the tongues ending in crocodile heads. As in the case of no. 224, there are two tails and the feet are profile crocodile heads. In the body there are decorative panels.

Although it appears soldered, this piece was modelled in wax and cast as a unit.
Length, ca. 2¾ in. Pl. CIV, *bottom left center.*

226

CAST GOLD PENDANT with two heads. The upper represents a jaguar and the lower a crocodile. Body and arms apparently are human. Across the chests on both ends there are gorgets with zigzag patterns. These probably were made of beads like the gorgets of the Guaymí Indians today.
Length, 3 7/8 in. Pl. C, *right.*

227

CAST GOLD PENDANT showing a pair of armadillos holding a two-headed snake in their mouths.
Length, ca. 1 5/8 in. Pl. CIV, *below No. 222.*

228 (56)

CAST GOLD PENDANT shaped like the tooth of a sperm whale. The inhabitants of Panama prized whale-tooth ivory highly. They carved teeth to represent crocodiles and a Crocodile god. Also they added gold heads as settings over the roots of the tooth. As the ivory supply was limited, they employed substitutes such as the tapering tips of manatee ribs or carved stone. This specimen is a solid gold imitation, too thin to be very successful. Hollow cast specimens are known which are the size and shape of the natural whale's tooth.
Length, 4¼ in. Pl. C, *left.*

229

CAST GOLD PENDANT representing a monkey holding its tail over its head. This art motif appears most commonly in Veraguas gold, but it was known as far north as Mexico (Pl. LI).
Height, 2 3/8 in. Pl. CI, *top left.*

230

CAST GOLD PENDANT representing a monkey holding its tail over its head.
Height, 3 5/8 in. Pl. CI, *top center.*

231

CAST GOLD PENDANT representing a monkey completely encircled by its tail.
Height, ca. 2⅛ in. Pl. CI, *top right.*

232

CAST GOLD PENDANT representing a monkey holding its tail over its head. The tip of the tail is a serpent's head. Height, $3\frac{3}{16}$ in. Pl. CI, *bottom center.*

233 (66)

CAST GOLD HEAD of an animal, perhaps a dog. Length, $1\frac{1}{8}$ in. Pl. CII, *second row, right.*

234

CAST GOLD PENDANT representing a man. He holds a snake in each hand and treads on their bodies. He wears a huge semicircular headdress adorned with crocodile symbols.
Height, $2\frac{3}{8}$ in. Pl. CIII, *center.*

235

CAST GOLD PENDANT representing a man. His headdress incorporates two snakes.
Height, ca. $3\frac{1}{8}$ in. Pl. CI, *bottom left.*

236

CAST GOLD PENDANT representing a man. He wears anklets and a headdress.
Height, $3\frac{1}{4}$ in. Pl. CI, *bottom right.*

237

CAST GOLD PENDANT representing a man with large ear ornaments.
Height, ca. $2\frac{3}{4}$ in. Pl. CIV, *top right center.*

238

CAST GOLD PENDANT representing a man with a rattle and flute.
Height, ca. $2\frac{3}{16}$ in. Pl. CIV, *bottom right center.*

239 (54)

CAST GOLD PENDANT showing an anthropomorphic Jaguar god. There were several deities of this type in Veraguas. They usually are shown 'framed' by repeating the outline of the headdress in reverse under the feet. There is no historical evidence concerning the powers and functions of these gods.
Height, $2\frac{5}{16}$ in. Pl. CII, *top left.*

240

CAST GOLD PENDANT representing a jaguar flanked by two pairs of crocodile heads.
Height, $2\frac{1}{8}$ in. Pl. CII, *top right.*

241

CAST GOLD PENDANT representing a Bird god who holds two serpents in his hands and beak.
Height, $2\frac{5}{16}$ in. Pl. CII, *top center.*

242 (53)

CAST GOLD PENDANT representing a Crocodile god.
Height, $1\frac{5}{8}$ in. Pl. CII, *bottom right.*

243

CAST GOLD PENDANT representing a Bird god.
Height, $2\frac{7}{8}$ in. Pl. CIV, *top right.*

244

CAST GOLD PENDANT representing a Crocodile god.
Height, $2\frac{7}{16}$ in. Pl. CIV, *bottom right.*

245

CAST GOLD BELL surmounted by a deer.
Height, ca. $2\frac{1}{8}$ in. Pl. CIV, *bottom left.*

246

CAST GOLD BELL representing a turtle with two tails.
Length, $2\frac{15}{16}$ in. Pl. CV, *bottom right.*

247

CAST GOLD BELL representing a turtle with two tails.
Length, ca. 3 in. Pl. CV, *bottom left.*

248 (64)

CAST GOLD BELL representing a turtle.
Length, $3\frac{7}{8}$ in. Pl. CV, *top right.*

249

SMALL CAST GOLD BELL surmounted by a bird.
Height, ca. 1 in. Pl. CV, *center.*

250

CAST GOLD BELL representing a double-headed eagle.
Width, ca. 4 in. Pl. CV, *top left.*

251 (67)

EMBOSSED DISK OF HAMMERED GOLD. Columbus secured over fifty of these on the north coast of Veraguas during his last voyage.
Diam., 8 in. Pl. CVI, *top left*.

252

EMBOSSED DISK OF HAMMERED GOLD.
Diam., 9 in. Pl. CVI, *top right*.

253

EMBOSSED DISK OF HAMMERED GOLD.
Diam., 9$\frac{5}{16}$ in. Pl. CVI, *bottom left*.

254

EMBOSSED DISK OF HAMMERED GOLD with an animal in relief.
Diam., 8$\frac{3}{4}$ in. Pl. CVI, *bottom right*.

255

DISK OF HAMMERED GOLD with four large bosses and four faces.
Diam., 10$\frac{9}{16}$ in. Pl. CVII, *left*.

256

DISK OF HAMMERED GOLD with four squatting figures embossed and stippled.
Diam., 7$\frac{3}{16}$ in. Pl. CVII, *top right*.

257

EMBOSSED AND STIPPLED GOLD DISK.
Diam., 5$\frac{1}{32}$ in. Pl. CVII, *bottom right*.

258

EMBOSSED AND STIPPLED GOLD DISK with two animal figures.
Diam., 4$\frac{1}{16}$ in. Pl. CVII, *bottom center*.

259

MINUTE GOLD BEADS cast in the forms of frogs, double frogs, an armadillo and a human head. Each has a small loop for stringing at the back. They are illustrated 1$\frac{1}{4}$ times actual size in Pl. CXI, and with a ca. × 5 magnification at the bottom of the page.
These specimens and others from the vicinity are the smallest castings known from aboriginal America, rank-ing with the minute gold beads produced in Ecuador. In view of early sixteenth-century trade between the two countries, it is possible that the technique passed from one to the other, perhaps in the form of a goldsmith-slave. The Veraguas beads evidently were of local manu-facture, for they embody local motifs. There are no marks of manufacture except in the case of the double frog (*bottom center*) where the channel for pouring the metal can be seen on one of the noses.
Cucayal, north of Soná, Province of Veraguas, Panama. Pl. CXI, *center right and bottom*.

The objects in Pls. CVIII–CX, CXII–CXIII inclusive are all in the style of Coclé.

260 (68)

CAST GOLD PENDANT representing a two-headed crocodile. The upper head is swallowing a child.
Length, 3 in. Pl. CVIII, *top right*.

261 (69)

CAST GOLD PENDANT showing a man drinking from a bottle. He wears a bead gorget.
Height, 2$\frac{1}{2}$ in. Pl. CVIII, *bottom right*.

262

PLAQUE OF GOLD BEATEN IN RELIEF. The design represents an anthropomorphic deity with crocodile claws replacing the hands and feet. The headdress is most unusual, for it consists of a pair of mouths with eyes attached to them, both placed vertically. Fish-like bodies extend from these mouths to frame the principal figure. On the basis of motifs found on pottery vessels, it is possible to identify these fish as hammer-head sharks. Historical records indicate that similar disks of gold were worn in the sixteenth century and no doubt for several centuries previously. In war each individual adorned himself as conspicuously as possible with such disks in order to be easily recognized and that his bravery would not be overlooked.
*Found at Sitio Conte on the Rio Grande de Coclé in 1954. Coclé Province, Panama. Diam., ca. 6$\frac{3}{4}$ in. Pl. CIX, *bottom*.

263

DISK OF HAMMERED GOLD decorated with a monstrous figure. The triangular head and the pair of curling tongues are associated in Coclé art with serpents or turtles, but, in this case, the tongues have been transferred from the sides of the mouth to the top of the head. Shoulders, arms and legs are represented as human except for the saurian claws on the hands and big toes. The body has been totally eliminated and the legs spring directly from the shoulders.

In most Coclé anthropomorphic figures, the body is definitely shown as well as a belt with dangling ends attached to small animal figures. In this specimen with no body, the belt appears as an independent unit below and beside the feet, so placed that it is in harmony with the design as a whole. The fringe on the belt is a conventionalization of crocodile scales. The small animals can be identified as sea horses. Each of the features enumerated probably had meaning to the maker, but the symbolism is lost to us today.
Venado Beach, Canal Zone. Diam., 6 in. Pl. CVIII, *left.*

264

MINUTE PENDANT OF CAST GOLD.
Venado Beach, Canal Zone. Actual size. Pl. CX, *top center.*

265

CAST GOLD PENDANT representing three cebus monkeys.
Venado Beach, Canal Zone. Actual size. Pl. CX, *center.*

266

CAST GOLD PENDANT representing a composite monstrous figure. The head, shoulders, arms and hands appear to be human. The body seems to be that of a snake, with a slight bulge to indicate it had recently fed. The pointed tail, however, turns out to be the head and beak of a bird with a crest on its head. Small solid wings are shown (Pl. CX, *top*) and the eyes are on stalks like those of a crab. Grasped in the hands of this strange apparition is a horizontal bar from which hang four danglers. The construction of this specimen is scarcely less curious than its form. With the exception of small areas such as face, hands, wings and head crests, the entire surface consists of wire-like scrolls. At first glance these appear to be soldered. In fact, however, they were laboriously built of wax threads over an interior core of clay and charcoal and then were encased in an outer core with the proper vents. The whole piece, except the danglers, was cast in a single flow of metal. Afterwards, both molds were broken and removed. A slit had been left in the back (Pl. CX, *top right*) through which fragments of the inner core could be extracted.

This specimen evidently was the work of a master craftsman, well versed in the lore and symbolism of his people. Only through the highest skill could the dozens

of wax threads have been laid to form a symmetrical whole. In placing them, not only aesthetic form had to be kept in mind but they had to be so ordered that molten metal would flow throughout the tiny channels.
Venado Beach, Canal Zone. Actual size. Height, $3\frac{3}{16}$ in.
Pl. CX, *top left and right, bottom left and right.*

267

SHELL PENDANT representing a crested bird.
Venado Beach, Canal Zone. Length, $1\frac{1}{2}$ in.
Pl. CXIII, *bottom right.*

268

PENDANT MADE OF A CLAM SHELL carved to represent a frog. The outer surface except the spine has been worked down all over.
Venado Beach, Canal Zone. Width, $2\frac{9}{16}$ in.
Pl. CXIII, *bottom left.*

269

NOSE PENDANT representing a turtle with a double scroll tongue. This piece must have been mounted on a base, perhaps of wood, and clipped to the septum of the nose by the slit in the top. It had been broken at the base in ancient times. Four small holes had been drilled by which the two pieces could be lashed together. This specimen also is unusual because it repeats in shell a type of ornament well-known in gold in the Province of Coclé.
Venado Beach, Canal Zone. Width, ca. $3\frac{1}{8}$ in.
Pl. CX, *bottom center.*

270

SHELL (whale-tooth ivory?) PENDANT representing a crocodile with bifurcated tail. Like no. 269, this also is a type of ornament hitherto only known in gold. A double-headed example is seen in Pl. CVIII, *top right.* It is not known why the tail tip of the animal is regularly shown as split, nor can the rectangular blocks projecting from the tail be explained.
Venado Beach, Canal Zone. Length, 8 in. Pl. CXII, *bottom.*

271

NECKLACE OF OLIVELLA SHELLS. Each individual shell has been drilled through the lip for stringing and the butt ends have been ground down to expose the interior spiral structure. In the center is a 'pig tail' which hung down the back of the owner when the necklace was discovered in the ground. This is a feature also found

among the Maya during the Classical period. Olivella shells, both cut in the fashion of this necklace or simply drilled, were prized both in North and South America, and they were widely distributed through trade. Usually they were combined with beads of other materials and complete necklaces are rare.
Venado Beach, Canal Zone. Scale, ca. ⅔. Pl. CXII, top.

272

GORGET OF CONCH SHELL. Each unit was cut from the thickest part of the outer curve of the shell and an adjacent part of the interior core. The cores were then so grooved that they suggest four rows of small beads.
This piece was found encircling a man's neck and projecting equally on all sides. Present-day Indians in Panama wear bead gorgets, either rectangular or semicircular, which cover the chest only and are not comparable. Carved boars'-tusk necklaces are known from ancient and modern times, but they were assembled with the flat side of the tusk parallel to the body.
Venado Beach, Canal Zone. Width, 8 in. Length of units from 2⅜ to 4 7/16 in. Pl. CXIII, top.

273

AGATE WINGED PENDANT. Among the most beautiful aboriginal jewelry from Panama are various objects of tawny agate. Most of these have been exposed to fire during the funeral ceremonies and have turned into an opaque marble.
The winged pendants are oval in section and pentagonal or oval in outline with a small knob on top which was pierced, for stringing. They are a local variant of a widespread group already discussed which symbolizes the outspread wings of a bat. See nos. 177, 178 and 208.
Sitio Conte on the Rio Grande de Coclé, Coclé Province, Panama. Length, 3 1/16 in. Pl. CIX, top.

COLOMBIA

See p. 33

274 (84)

NECKLACE OF GOLD BIRDS. These seem to have been hammered to shape in a mold. The stringing is modern.
Chibcha style. Colombia. Slightly enlarged. Pl. CXI.

275 (82)

CAST GOLD ANIMAL, probably a toy.
Chibcha style. Colombia. Length, 2⅜ in.
Pl. CXIV, *top left.*

276

CAST GOLD FIGURE OF A MAN, probably a toy. He carries two spears and a spear thrower.
Chibcha style. Colombia. Height, 1½ in. Pl. CXIV, top left.

277

CAST GOLD FIGURE OF A MAN, probably a toy.
Chibcha style. Colombia. Height, 1⅞ in.
Pl. CXIV, *center left.*

278 (81)

CAST GOLD FIGURE OF A BIRD, probably a toy.
Chibcha style. Colombia. Length, 1⅞ in.
Pl. CXIV, *center.*

279

CAST GOLD PENDANT representing four bird heads attached to a single tail. There is a tube at the back through which a string was run for suspension.
Chibcha style. Colombia. Width, 4 in.
Pl. CXIV, *bottom left.*

280

GOLD PENDANT representing an eagle.
Colombia. Width, 4 in. Pl. CXIV, top right.

281

GOLD NOSE PENDANT? This type was inserted in the septum and hung with the ends down (Pl. CXVIII).
Colombia. Width, ca. 2⅜ in. Pl. CXIV, bottom right.

282 (72)

NECKLACE OF CAST GOLD BEADS.
Quimbaya style. Colombia. Slightly enlarged. Pl. CXI.

283 (74)

CAST GOLD PENDANT representing a bird.
Quimbaya style. Colombia. Height, 1⅛ in.
Pl. CXI, *top left.*

284

CAST GOLD PENDANT. This probably is one from a series of identical forms once made into a necklace.
Quimbaya style. Colombia. Length, 1⅛ in.
Pl. CXI, *top right.*

285

CAST GOLD BIRD on a socket. This evidently was placed on a wooden shaft.
Quimbaya style. Colombia. Height, 3$\frac{5}{16}$ in. Pl. CXV, *top.*

286

CAST GOLD BIRD with head plumes, standing on a socket.
Quimbaya style. Colombia. Height, 3$\frac{15}{16}$ in.
Pl. CXV, *bottom.*

287 (77)

PIN OR SCEPTER OF CAST GOLD. The head consists of a coiled snake on which stands a crocodile with upraised tail. A smaller crocodile stands on the back of the larger.
Colima style. Colombia. Length, 7$\frac{3}{4}$ in. Pl. CXVI, *right.*

288 (78)

CAST GOLD PIN OR SCEPTER. Like no. 287, the head consists of a coiled snake, in this case with the body markings indicated. On the snake is an animal with upraised tail, perhaps a crocodile or a turtle. A smaller version of the same animal stands on its back.
Colima style. Colombia. Length, 11$\frac{3}{8}$ in. Pl. CXVI, *left.*

289 (71)

CAST GOLD NOSE PENDANT with birds at the end.
Quimbaya style. Colombia. Length, 5$\frac{3}{8}$ in.
Pl. CXVI, *center.*

290

CAST GOLD PENDANT representing an anthropomorphic deity. Several examples of this complex form are known, one of which was traded as far north as Yucatan. The mouth and nose, indicated by spirals, may symbolize a crocodile. On either side are spirals which probably indicate bird wings. The two dome-shaped objects on the head are unidentified. A pair of tubes issuing from the mouth may be flutes or whistles. The legs and feet may be considered human.
Darien style, probably from the upper Atrato valley. Colombia. Height, 5$\frac{1}{16}$ in. Pl. CXVII, *bottom right.*

291 (79)

CAST GOLD PENDANT, a miniature of no. 290.
Colombia. Height, 1 in. Pl. CXVII, *center.*

Fig. 24. *Profile of gold breast plate* illustrated in Pl. CXVIII. Colima style. Colombia. (Cat. No. 295.)

292 (73)

CAST GOLD PENDANT representing twin animals.
Sinú style. Colombia. Length, 2$\frac{7}{8}$ in. Pl. CXVII, *top right.*

293

CAST GOLD PENDANT representing a bird.
Sinú style. Colombia. Width, ca. 2$\frac{3}{8}$ in.
Pl. CXVII, *bottom left.*

294 (76)

STYLIZED GOLD PENDANT. The face appears to be human but the bifurcated tail – see Pl. CXII, *bottom* – and the head crests are features associated with the crocodile. Suppression of all detail except on the face is characteristic of the style, and sometimes even the head is featureless.

Style of Tolima. Colombia. Height, 6$\frac{7}{16}$ in.

Pl. CXVII, *top left.*

295 (85)

BREAST PLATE OF HAMMERED SHEET GOLD. There is a border pattern in low relief, apparently of zoömorphic origin, which vaguely recalls the motifs seen in Pl. CVII, *top right.* In the center there is a human head hammered in very high relief, a characteristic also of some of the sheet gold from Ecuador. This head is adorned with a cap, two wire nose rings and a pair of gold plates attached to the ears by wire rings.

Conto style. Colombia. Width, 12$\frac{1}{2}$ in.

Pl. CXVIII and fig. 24.

VENEZUELA

See p. 35

296

MASSIVE TUMBAGA PENDANT representing an anthropomorphic Crocodile god. The body is essentially human but the head is a mass of symbolism except the mouth and teeth. The upper part of the face apparently is a mask with a diamond-shape plaque over the nose and two bird torsos over the eyes. This is held in place by a braided cord seen on either side of the face (fig. 25). At the base of the mask there are small rings, probably for the attachment of danglers.

Flanking the head are a pair of wings which suggest animal heads in profile. On the tips there are small tubes suitable for holding feathers. Above the head are elaborate crests, broken at the tips so that their exact nature cannot now be ascertained. One of the tips carries a small tube like those on the wings.

This unusual ornament was built up in wax over a clay core and cast as a unit except the gold balls on the wings, head plumes and on the ornaments carried in the hands. These were fashioned separately with a short tang projecting from them and were riveted in place after the casting was finished. They are of purer gold than the casting.

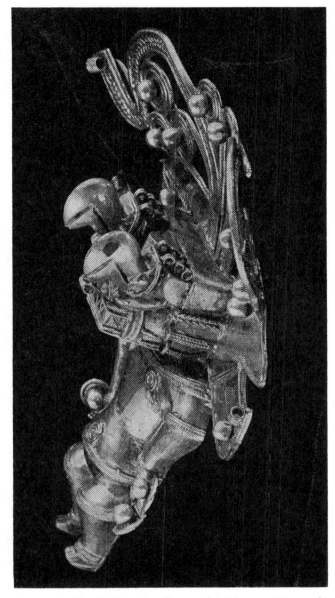

Fig. 25. *Profile of gold pendant* illustrated in Pl. CXIX. Venezuela. (Cat. No. 296.)

Vicinity of Maracaibo?, Venezuela. The style resembles that attributed to the Tairona of Colombia but is much more massive. Height ca. 6$\frac{1}{16}$ in. Pl. CXIX, and fig. 25.

PERU

See p. 35

297

SOAPSTONE CUP. On the outer walls is a pair of two-headed, eight-legged animals. On the base is a head with large canine teeth, perhaps a conventionalized jaguar.

Cupisnique (coastal Chavin) culture. North coast of Peru. Height, 3$\frac{5}{16}$ in. Pl. CXX, *top,* and CXXI, *top.*

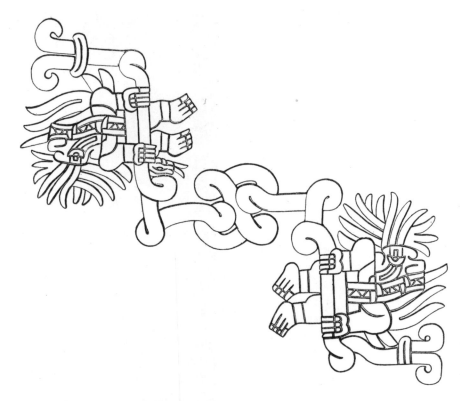

Fig. 26. *Extended design from soapstone cup* illustrated in Pl. cxx, *bottom*. (Cat. No. 298.) By William Baake.

298

SOAPSTONE CUP. On the outer walls is a pair of figures with human limbs and jaguar heads adorned with plumes. Each holds a snake-like body with many loops which extends from one to the other across the base of the vessel. The extended design appears in fig. 26.
Cupisnique (coastal Chavin) culture. North coast of Peru. Height, $4\frac{1}{8}$ in. Pl. CXX, *bottom*, and fig. 26.

299

DIORITE CLUB HEAD with four blades and eight spikes. This form may represent a cactus.
Cupisnique (coastal Chavin) culture. North coast of Peru. Height, ca. $4\frac{15}{16}$ in. Pl. CXXI, *bottom*.

300

GOLD SPOON with a handle which portrays a man blowing a silver shell-trumpet. This piece is made of hammered sheets of metal soldered together to form a hollow figure. It represents the earliest known phase of this technique and it is the earliest known bimetallic object from the New World. An incised design on the back appears in fig. 27.
Chavin culture. Peru. Length, $4\frac{7}{16}$ in. Pl. CXXII, *top right* and fig. 27.

301

GOLD DISK found with no. 300. In the central circular panel there is a much conventionalized face with serpents issuing from the mouth. An angular guilloche runs around the border. It was beaten in relief from the back but the central panel is intaglio, for the background has been driven in from the front.
Chavin culture. Peru. Diam., $4\frac{13}{16}$ in. Pl. CXXII, *bottom center*.

Fig. 27. *Design incised on back of figure* in Pl. cxxii, *top right*. (Cat. No. 300.)

302

BEATEN GOLD DISK adorned with a guilloche. This was one of a set of fourteen, discovered later than the others, but in the same place. It is clearly related in shape and decoration to the disk in Pl. CXXII, but some of the associated objects indicate that it dates from the beginning of the Mochica period.
Very late Chavin culture. Found on a hilltop east of the Pan American Highway a few miles north of Huarmey. Diam., 8 3/16 in. Pl. CXXIII, center.

303

HAMMERED GOLD PLAQUE. Two masked warriors are shown dancing around a pole which each grasps in one hand. The pole is surmounted by a grinning head, and near the base is a little dog which appears to be dancing. Both individuals wear belts terminating in animal heads. One carries a conch-shell trumpet (?) suspended from his elbow.
This object is not complete in itself, as there are holes for attachment to something on two sides and slots on a third. On the fourth side there are two projecting tongues which have been clinched over some dark substance, perhaps leather.
Mochica culture. North coast of Peru. Width, 4 5/8 in. Pl. CXXII, top left.

304

INCISED AND INLAID BONE HANDLE in the form of a clenched fist. The forefinger crosses over the middle finger. The nails are inlays. Originally this was the handle of a narrow chisel-like blade, now broken off.
Mochica culture. North coast of Peru. Length, 3 3/4 in. Pl. CXXII, bottom right and left.

305 (144)

FOURTEEN SMALL HEADS OF HAMMERED GOLD. These must have been beaten to shape over a mold. Each has several small holes in the sides by which they could have been firmly attached to a base, perhaps a woven headband.
Mochica (?) culture. North coast of Peru. Height, 1 11/16 in. Pl. CXXIII.

306 (138)

STIRRUP-MOUTH POTTERY JAR. Modelled and painted vessels with a hollow loop handle topped by a short spout are typical of the north coast of Peru. During the Mochica era, the subjects portrayed were of great variety and often rendered with considerable realism. The present specimen shows two gulls quarrelling over a fish.
Mochica culture. North coast of Peru. Height, 8 7/8 in. Pl. CXXV, right.

307

PAIR OF SHEET-GOLD OBJECTS, perhaps dance wands. These pieces are of thin flexible sheet-gold except the handles which are stiff, although not very massive. The subject, well-known in Nazca and Paracas-Necropolis art, is the so-called cat demon. He is shown with extended tongue flanked by spiral fangs, four legs and the outspread wings and tail of a bird. At the tips of the wings long feathers are represented, but the remaining edges of wing are filled by simple heads, just mouth and eyes, assembled in groups of five. These may have been regarded as trophy heads and the lines connecting them would then represent the rope on which such heads were suspended.
Identification as dance wands is based on Paracas textiles and Nazca pottery on which individuals often are shown holding pairs of identical objects in their hands.
Paracas-Necropolis style or early Nazca. Width, 10 5/8 in. Pl. CXXIV.

308 (201)

PENDANT OF INLAID SHELL SET IN GOLD. A face is embossed in the setting. Most of the inlay consists of small beads and turquoise.
Nazca style, Period B. South coast of Peru. Length, 3 3/4 in. Pl. CXXXIII, bottom left.

309 (206)

POTTERY JAR representing a skull. The presentation is highly stylized with little attempt at modelling or anatomical accuracy. No elements of Tiahuanaco style are present except the tall flaring spouts and circular eyes which are characteristic of vessels produced during the period when that style flourished on the Peruvian littoral.
South coast of Peru. Height, 6 1/4 in. Pl. CXXV, left.

310

MOSAIC MIRROR of pyrites, turquoise and shell. The mosaic covers a base of wood, cut in one piece, which has been identified as Betulaceae: *Alnus jorullensis* HBK, an alder locally known in Peru as *aliso, tambran* or *ramran*. Although this tree grows at considerable altitudes, the poorly defined growth rings in this specimen indicate that the wood came from the arid coast, which is watered not by seasonal rains but by irrigation. Extensive deterioration of the cell walls shows that the wood has an age of several centuries.

The mosaic originally was held in place by some kind of resin which it has not been possible to identify botanically. This is intact and firm under the reflecting surface and elsewhere. In part, however, the mosaic had peeled off and had been replaced with modern glue, during which process there may have been some restoration. Some of the individual pieces of shell had small holes pierced by marine borers. These had been plugged, presumably in ancient times.

Mosaic mirrors of pyrites (fool's gold) were manufactured in Mexico, northern Central America, Panama, Peru, and probably elsewhere. They date back to Classical Maya times but are nowhere common. Examples on a base of wood are known only from Peru. Specimens from wetter regions have bases of stone, and the reflecting surface usually has been damaged by rust.

The example here illustrated has a reflecting surface framed by a band of geometric patterns. On the opposite side there is a stylized face of a type known in pottery and textile designs. The rectangular head and tear streaks below the eyes terminating in small heads are characteristic features. Also the circular eyes. The handle terminates in a serpent head. Body markings of a snake are suggested by decoration on the four sides of the handle and on the edges of the mirror frame. This specimen formerly was in the Moises Saenz collection.

Coastal Tiahuanaco style. Central or south coast of Peru. Length, 9⅜ in. Pls. CXXVI and CXXVII.

Numbers 311 to 322 inclusive comprise a group of gold ornaments and utensils, some of unique type, found in a grave of the Chimu period (thirteenth to sixteenth century) near Huarmey, about 160 miles north of Lima. These fall into two distinct groups: (1) the adornments of the outer wrappings of the mummy bundle, including a mask, a pair of elaborate ear ornaments and an equally elaborate gorget or breast ornament as well as a large number of loose sequins; and (2) articles for the use of their owner after death, comprising a headband, two large rings or bangles, a nose pendant, a point for a digging stick, a spear-thrower and a small but massive slab of gold for rolling wax. This group of gold ornaments includes some of the most complex objects from Peru. The four artifacts which adorned the surface of the mummy bundle were manufactured by joining over six hundred individual pieces of gold, including over two hundred danglers. The total effect of the big gold surfaces in sunlight, enhanced by smaller movable and flashing sheets, must indeed have appeared sumptuous even in the eyes of a people well-accustomed to seeing ornaments of gold.

311

GOLD MUMMY MASK. The mask is the simplest of the objects attached to the mummy bundle. The headdress is made of three separate sheets, a central core and two wings, which are attached to the forehead by three metal ribbons. It is adorned by nine embossed geometric patterns which are derived from a fish motif, and originally it carried twenty-six danglers hung from wires which were soldered to the background and projected upward at about a forty-five-degree angle. The eyes are cut out. The eyebrows are small rolled sheets of metal with two tabs projecting at each end by means of which they were clinched in place. Each eyebrow is surmounted by four small danglers on wires. The lips also are rolled sheets clinched in place. The nose is a rolled sheet, trimmed at the base to show nostrils and to provide tabs for clinching it to the face. On the sides of the nose there are two metal straps. Ears are indicated by semicircular projections. Additional decoration consists of a double-headed fish embossed on each cheek, and a simpler version of the same motif repeated five times on the chin. From ear to ear the face is outlined by a line of embossed diamonds with a pair of small perforations flanking each point of contact. What purpose they served is problematical, but evidently something is missing. This face was once attached to a mummy bundle presumably by four massive U-shaped loops projecting from the back. These pierced the metal sheet and were soldered to four small plaques on the front of the face beside the eyes and on the chin. *Chimu culture. Huarmey, Peru. Height, 12⅝ in. Pl. CXXVIII.*

312

COMPLEX GOLD BREAST PLATE. The base is a single metal sheet, roughly trapezoidal in shape, with circular disks incorporated at the corners. An embossed diamond pattern outlines the main part of the gorget, an inner enclosed area and the four corner disks. The outer edges of the disks show a variant of the pattern with terraced outlines and small cut-out areas. In the center of the gorget is a face framed in a shield-shape border. The embossed mouth seems to be that of a feline animal. Nose and eyes are of unusual form. Each eye consists of a metal socket in which is set a rod of shell about two inches long, presumably the columella of a conch shell. Each rod is capped by a hemispherical sheet of gold with five danglers and a small bird perched on the end (fig. 28). The base of the nose is a square raised platform clinched in place on the sides and on top and bottom. Thirteen danglers were soldered to the upper part. Below these is a

Fig. 28. *Side view of breastplate* illustrated in Pl. CXXIX.
(Cat. No. 312.)

313, 314

PAIR OF COMPLEX GOLD EAR ORNAMENTS. The ornate ear ornaments obviously are of the same style and workmanship as no. 312. The border pattern of the disks is the same as that of the corner disks on the gorget. Each ear disk is adorned with embossed danglers of the same design as those of the gorget, forming three concentric circles with ten, eight and six danglers. In the center of each disk is a rod cut from a conch columella, which is tipped by a gold cap and bird and two danglers. A band of small beads encircles the shell column on each ear disk. From each disk hangs a metal plaque, which is attached by two wire rings. The plaques are embossed in the same diamond pattern as the disks and the gorget, and each has six danglers. Suspended from each plaque by pairs of wire rings are six parallel serpents with zigzag bodies terminating in human faces. Attached to each mouth is a dangler of the same design as the rest.
Chimu culture. Huarmey, Peru. Length, 10 in.
Pl. CXXX, *top*, and fig. 29.

Fig. 29. *Side view of ear ornament* illustrated in Pl. CXXX.
(Cat. No. 313-14.)

circular plaque with raised scalloped edge, adorned with ten danglers and a bird made of shell and a bird made of shell and gold. Other danglers on the gorget were distributed as follows: two rows of eighteen each across the top of the central area, and ten on each lower disk. Each dangler (one hundred and eleven altogether) has the shape of a stepped cross with an embossed diamond in the center, a form which seems to repeat the embossed border pattern, and especially the variant form found on the outer edges of the four corner disks. On either side of the face is a small rectangular plaque from which a wire loop projects in back. These are exactly like the loops on the back of the mask (no. 311) and imply that the same craftsman made both pieces. It is probable that the gorget, on account of its greater weight, received additional support by stitching through the cut-out borders of the disks into a cloth background.
Chimu culture. Huarmey, Peru. Width, ca. 15⅛ in.
Pl. CXXIX and fig. 28.

315

A GROUP OF MORE THAN 1,200 SEQUINS. Each is pierced by two small holes and probably was sewn on a cloth background. The use of metal sequins became quite common on the central coast of Peru. Normally they were attached to headbands or ponchos, often arranged to form simple patterns.
Chimu culture. Huarmey, Peru. Diam., $\frac{15}{32}$ in.
Pl. CXXX, *bottom.*

316

HEADBAND OF GOLD BEADS AND TUBES. Each of the one hundred and twenty-six beads consists of two hammered hemispheres soldered together. The tubes are joined to each other and to end plates so that each group is a solid unit. Three hundred and eighteen individual pieces of metal were combined to form this headband.
Chimu culture. Huarmey, Peru. Length, $14\frac{7}{8}$ in.
Pl. CXXXI, *left center.*

317

PAIR OF GOLD BANGLES. These are hollow and contain rattles. A peculiar feature is that each has a slit through which a rectangular plaque can be inserted. What purpose this served and how they were worn is uncertain. From their size one would expect them to go on the legs, but the plaques may be a device for holding them on the upper arm.
Chimu culture. Huarmey, Peru. Diam., 5 in.
Pl. CXXXI, *top* and *right.*

318

NOSE PENDANT of gold, stone and shell. The gold is a setting for the other materials. Nose ornaments are not common in the Chimu period.
Chimu culture. Huarmey, Peru. Diam. $1\frac{3}{8}$ in.
Pl. CXXXII, *second row, right.*

319

SPEAR-THROWER of wood with gold sheathing. The type is very different from that used in Mexico (Pl. XLIX). Both examples may have had a pair of loops on the handle for inserting the fingers.
Chimu culture. Huarmey, Peru. Length, $22\frac{1}{2}$ in.
Pl. CXXXI, *center* and *bottom.*

320

GOLD STOPPER for a lime case. Similar rods with a knob or loop at the end have been found in small lime cases made of gourds. Usually they are of wood or bone. Coca chewing was and is common in Peru. Lime always is mixed with the leaves.
Chimu culture. Huarmey, Peru. Length, $3\frac{1}{2}$ in.
Pl. CXXXII, *top right.*

321

GOLD TIP for a digging stick. The plow was unknown in Peru and all planting was done in holes made with a pointed stick. Seeds and guano or a small fish for fertilizer were dropped in the hole. Metal tips for the stick are fairly common in the Chimu area, but usually they are of copper or bronze. This specimen has retained some of the pitch used to attach it to the wood.
Chimu culture. Huarmey, Peru. $3\frac{3}{4}$ in.
Pl. CXXXII, *second row, left center.*

322

SOLID GOLD SLAB. This is not an ingot but a utensil, as all surfaces have been carefully smoothed and polished, whereas Peruvian ingots are rough castings. This gold block is almost exactly matched in size and shape by a rhyolite slab with a highly polished surface which was found with a set of Peruvian metal-working tools. Slabs like these are identified as the bases on which wax sheets were rolled, 'thin like the web of a spider', to model objects cast by the *cire perdue* process. The presence of this specimen in the funeral furnishings indicates that the owner was a practising goldsmith, and it suggests that he himself might have had a hand in shaping the metal objects buried with him.
Chimu culture. Huarmey, Peru. Length, $2\frac{5}{8}$ in.
Pl. CXXXII, *second row, right center.*

323 (140)

GOLD HEADBAND AND PIN shaped like a feather. The use of gold headbands and crowns in Peru extends back to the Chavin period.
Chimu culture. Coast of Peru. Height as illustrated, 14 in.
Pl. CXXXII, *bottom, right center.*

324

GOLD AND SILVER PIN. The shaft, most of the semi-circular head and the nine danglers are silver; the rest is gold. The metal is very thin but the line of juncture can scarcely be seen, and there is no trace of solder. The embossing, which was done after the joining, displays animal heads at the tips of the plumes and corners of the semicircular parts.
Chimu culture. North coast of Peru. Total length, 13 in. Length of gold, 5 in. Pl. CXXXII, *right.*

325

GOLD PIN adorned with a face. This piece is intact but the shaft has been doubled back.
Coast of Peru. Length, 5¾ in. Pl. CXXXII, *top left.*

326 (145)

GOLD CUP with a frieze of birds around the rim.
Chimu culture. North coast of Peru. Height, 4¼ in. Pl. CXXXII, *bottom left.*

327 (146)

GOLD CUP with face in relief.
Coast of Peru. Height, 6¹⁄₁₆ in. Pl. CXXXII, *bottom, left center.*

328

MASSIVE GOLD VESSEL, representing a half gourd. The body has been beaten to shape from a single piece of metal. The rim was made separately and has been soldered in place. It is adorned with incised terraced frets. The cut-out section of the rim makes it easier either to drink or to pour. Gourds of this size and shape are often used today to serve liquor stored in large jars to individual drinkers.
Coast of Peru. Length, 7 in. Pl. CXXXIV, *bottom.*

329 (143)

HOLLOW SILVER BIRDS, perhaps part of a necklace.
Coast of Peru. Length, 1⁵⁄₁₆ in. Pl. CXXXIV, *top.*

330

TWO PLAQUES of a copper-silver alloy with symbolic designs in relief. Nail holes suggest that they had been attached to something as sheathing. In aboriginal Peru, entire rooms sometimes were plated in gold or silver. Entire edifices might be encircled by wide bands of sheet metal.
Chimu style. North coast of Peru. Scale, ca. ⁶⁄₇. Pl. CXXXIX.

331

BONE FLUTE with notched ends. The inlay is shell. Both flutes and pan-pipes were in common use throughout Peru.
Coast of Peru. Length, 3¼ in. Pl. CXXXVIII, *top right.*

332

INLAID SHELL PENDANT. Two gulls are shown devouring fish.
Chimu culture. North coast of Peru. Width, 3¹⁵⁄₁₆ in. Pl. CXXXIV, *center.*

333 (153)

BALANCE-BEAM SCALES. The ancient inhabitants of Mexico, although they had developed a currency, did not buy and sell by weight. In parts of South America, however, two types of scales were known. In Venezuela and Colombia, also probably in Ecuador and extreme northern Peru, the steelyard or Roman scales were employed to weigh metal. Further south in Peru, balance scales were in use.

The example here discussed has a carved bone beam with an incised circle and dot pattern used in late periods on the coast. The silhouetted figures along the top edge were a version of the portrayal of the ibis, a bird perhaps of some symbolic significance in the late periods. Nets are constructed of Z-spun S-doubled bast fiber, with an overhand knot and a mesh of ½ inch knot to knot.

This type would be suitable for weighing such commodities as coca leaves, cotton or wool. Scales have been found with small metal pans instead of nets, which probably were designed for weighing metals.

It has been established that in Peru a definite series of stone weights was used, based on a unit of about 3.80 grams, with larger weights up to eighteen and twenty-five times that amount. Tests have shown that scales like the example illustrated will react to as little as 0.05 grams.
Chimu culture. Length of beam, 4⁷⁄₈ in. Pl. CXXXVIII, *center.*

334

BEAM FOR BALANCE SCALE. This specimen is of cast copper inlaid with shell. The threads for suspension are modern. In two square panels warriors are represented, each holding a pair of purses and spears. The inlay has been set in pitch.
Chimu culture. North coast of Peru. Length, 5 in. Pl. CXXXVIII, *left.*

335

SILVER PIN. The head displays a parrot perched on two ears of maize.
Coast of Peru. Length, 7¹⁄₃₂ in. Pl. CXXXIII, *right.*

336 (150)

COPPER OR BRONZE EAR SPOON with a bird on the handle.
Coast of Peru. Length, 2½ in. Pl. CXXXIII, *left.*

337

FIGURINE WITH GOLD AND SHELL INLAYS.
Chimu culture. North coast of Peru. Height, ca. 1⁵⁄₁₆ in. Pl. CXXXIII, *top center.*

338 (191)

HOLLOW SILVER FIGURINE. This exemplifies typical Inca workmanship, for it consists of several sheets of metal, hammered to shape individually and soldered together. Life-size statues representing the Inca rulers were seized by the Spaniards. The individual here represented is a nobleman, called *orejon* (big ears) by the Spaniards because they wore huge ear plugs which stretched the lobes of the ears.

Inca culture. Peru. Height, $8\frac{7}{8}$ in. Pl. CXXXV.

339 (199)

MACE HEAD in the form of bronze bird inlaid with copper and silver. The art of joining sheets of two metals such as gold and silver had been mastered in the Chavin period well before the Christian era. Inlaying of one or more metals in another, however, was a process discovered only just before the Conquest. Most of the known examples have come from the southern mountains of Peru and some definitely are Inca in style. The example here illustrated has been called an adze, but the 'blade' formed by the tail of the bird apparently never has been sharpened.

Peru. Width, $4\frac{7}{8}$ in. Pl. CXXXVI, *top.*

340

GORGET OF GOLD AND SILVER inlaid in each other. Most inlaid objects are cast, with the result that there is a solid base to work on. This piece, however, is a hammered sheet scarcely a millimeter in thickness. The subject is a favorite one in Peru – fish and birds.

Peru. Width, $7\frac{1}{8}$ in. Pl. CXXXVI, *bottom.*

341 (200)

BRONZE CHOPPING KNIFE inlaid with silver and copper. This type of knife, known as *tumi* to the Inca, is found all over Peru and appears to have been in common use for eating. The fact that this one terminates in a llama head and has small llamas and snakes inlaid on the shank suggests that it was used for sacrifices held to increase the flocks.

Peru. Width, $6\frac{1}{2}$ in. Pl. CXXXVII.

PERUVIAN TEXTILES

See p. 55

342 (220)

PAINTED CLOTH made specifically for burial. The square stylized figure has three pairs of zigzag snakes emerging from the head and another pair, probably representing a belt, at the sides. Snake symbolism is widespread, and although not explained historically in Peru, is associated with rain in Mexico and the southwestern United States. The cloth is of the type constructed for false head coverings on mummy bundles, and the unwoven ends were arranged as hair.

Warp and weft: Z-spun S-doubled cotton.

Count: 32×14.

Length: $26\frac{1}{2}$ in. Of the warp, 10 in. have been woven.

Width: $10\frac{3}{16}$ to $12\frac{1}{4}$ in.

Heading: (1) 1 cord at unfinished end, broken.
          (2) 3 cords each Z-spun S-doubled redoubled Z.

Paracas-Cavernas culture. South coast of Peru. Pl. CXL, *left.*

343 (219)

FRAGMENT OF AN EMBROIDERED MANTLE BORDER. The contorted dancing figures, with ribs indicated, hold staffs and fans in their hands. A needle-knitted tubular edging repeats the design. Since the lower and upper bodies are blue, there might have been a four-unit color rhythm. The triangular tabs are unique and must have been made by weaving or darning with a needle and probably required guide cords for their edges. The repeat is in a sequence of 3 red, 1 yellow, 1 olive green.

Warp and weft of basic fabric: Z-spun S-doubled cotton.

Embroidery yarns: Z-spun S-doubled wool.

Length: 21 in.

Width: $4\frac{1}{2}$ in. with pointed tab-fringes $1\frac{1}{2}$ in. long (both incomplete).

Paracas-Necropolis culture. South coast of Peru. Pl. CXL, *right.*

344

EMBROIDERED MANTLE. This mantle is one of the most elaborate of Paracas-Necropolis types in having embroidered figures on the main portion as well as on the border. The anthropomorphic figures with mouth masks, headdress, complex body appendages with hands holding trophy heads and clubs respectively are so closely related to parallel forms on early Nazca pottery as to demonstrate a close connection between the two cultures. In this specimen there is a definite repeat of seven in the colors of the figures.

Warp and weft of basic fabric: Z-spun S-doubled cotton.

Embroidery yarns: Z-spun S-doubled wool.

Count: 48×40 – main fabric.

36×32 – borders.

Dimensions: 110×52 in.

Paracas-Necropolis culture. South coast of Peru. Pl. CXLI.

345

TASSEL FOR TURBAN OR BELT STRAP of intertwined warp plaiting with needle-knitted details. The main portion is divided into three units of a complex feline (?) motif obscured by geometric details. Both this and no. 346 are extremely rare types. Apparently they were made in pairs, connected by a cord. Technically they are complex and beautifully made. Today, no single term in English has been applied to this technique. Construction procedure always results in two identical products, which are then sewn together at the sides. In this, two separate sets of warps are used, red and yellow, and by shifting these during construction two separate webs are produced as in double-cloth, but no weft is employed. After construction, the middle portion is covered with a needle-knitting technique.

Material: all Z-spun S-doubled wool.

Length: 13½ in.

Width: 4½ in. at top and 8¾ in. at bottom.

Nazca culture? South coast of Peru. Pl. CXLII, right.

346

TASSEL FOR TURBAN OR BELT STRAP of intertwined warp plaiting with twining and warp patterns. This is an even more complicated version than no. 345, since there is an addition of a warp pattern showing conventionalized birds. It almost defies description and demonstrates a feature frequently found in Peruvian fabrics, where enormous care is taken in details which cannot even be seen. In this case, for instance, the webs on the inside carry the same warp patterns under the plaited and twined sections, where they have no function, since the whole is sewn along its edges.

Material: all Z-spun S-doubled wool.

Length: 13½ in.

Width: at top 4½ in., at bottom 8¾ in.

Nazca culture? South coast of Peru. Pl. CXLII, left.

347 (231)

FRAGMENT OF TAPESTRY with interlocked weft and short slits. Puma head, claws and tail (?) in profile view are split so as to appear double-headed. The outlining in black of the red, bright blue and yellow is a characteristic feature of this style. In the body as well as the border there are stylized motifs in double-diamonds and three-pronged elements reminiscent of some late Nazca pottery designs.

Warp: Z-spun S-doubled, redoubled Z-cotton (?).

Weft: Z-spun S-doubled wool; cotton.

Count: 27×205 (variable).

Length: 12½ in.

Width: 12 in.

Heading: one multiple cord.

Blend of Late Nazca and Wari styles. South coast of Peru. Pl. CXLIII, top.

348

PONCHO SHIRT (?) of eccentric and interlocked weft tapestry. The large puma figures with design fillers of spreading scroll-like elements, as well as the split-animal figures, are not too often seen in complete specimens. The design, colors and outlines of black are in the same tradition as no. 347. Though this piece is now closed along the central seam, and has been mended in modern times with sections of other fabrics, it perhaps originally was a short poncho shirt. It is shown folded in half.

Warp: Z-spun S-doubled coarse heavy wool.

Weft: Z-spun S-doubled wool.

Count: 29×16.

Length: 30 in. (complete).

Width: 34 in.

Heading: (a) 3 cords.

(b) cut.

Blend of Late Nazca and Wari styles. South coast of Peru. Pl. CXLIII, bottom.

349

MAJOR PORTION OF PONCHO SHIRT of interlocked tapestry. Elaborately clothed Tiahuanaco staff-bearing figures are arranged in two bands, facing in opposite directions. Of semi-animal characteristics, bird and puma motifs abound in the headdress, on the tunic, and they also emerge from the tongue and staffs. This piece is unusual in having only two instead of four broad pattern units. However, the narrow borders, in this as well as all the other Tiahuanaco shirts illustrated, repeat the central motifs in compressed form. The crowding of elements at the outer sides of the figures in both panels is a common characteristic of coastal Tiahuanaco tapestries. It will be noted that details such as staffs which should balance each other in size in fact do not. This arises through faulty planning and weaving as will be explained in connection with no. 355. This piece is incomplete, and has been cut open at the sides.

Warp: Z-spun S-doubled cotton.

Weft: Z-spun S-doubled wool.

Count: 31×188 in.

Length: 22½ in. each loom length.

Width: 69½ in., incomplete, originally 84 in. (?).

Size as shown: 69½×45 in.

Coastal Tiahuanaco culture. Central or south coast of Peru. Pl. CXLIV. Detail, Pl. CXLV.

350

PORTION OF PONCHO SHIRT of interlocked tapestry with some slits and eccentric details. This is a particularly involved representative of the Tiahuanaco-type staff-bearing figures. There are six different types of figures including the neck pattern, the latter consisting of four semi-realistic puma figures, two facing one another and the other two inverted. It is a very striking piece in its color combinations, and unusual in the variation of figure and supplementary motif detail.

Warp: Z-spun S-doubled cotton.

Weft: Z-spun S-doubled wool.

Counts: 25–27×116–114.

Length: 21¼ in. each side.

Width: 58 in. incomplete (originally 84 in.?).

Heading: (1) interlocked loops.
            (2) cut and diagonally plaited.

Size as illustrated: 58×43½ in.

Late coastal Tiahuanaco culture. Central or south coast of Peru. Pl. CXLVI.

351

PONCHO SHIRT of interlocked and eccentric tapestry. This design derives from the full Tiahuanaco figures but is exceedingly abstract. The field is divided into bands of blocks in which are shown a 'weeping eye' and mouth, separated diagonally by a step-fret element. This general comment applies also to nos. 352, 353 and 354. In this specimen, a second motif appears in the form of sets of three double-heads with either the eyes only, or eyes and mouths indicated. On the right side of the shirt the eye is placed with the tear below it, whereas on the left, the entire order of the design is in reverse.

This is a complete shirt, made of two separately woven fabrics, joined together with the warp running across the shirt and sewn at the center. The particularly vivid pink, rose, and shades of blue and green are unique. The eccentric feature of the tapestry is outstanding: even the solid yellow stripes are marked in this respect, probably for texture effect.

Warp: Z-spun S-doubled wool, some cotton.

Weft: Z-spun S-doubled wool.

Count: 21×78.

Length: 20½ in. each side.

Width: 80 in.

Heading: (1) interlocked loops at center of the shirt.
            (2) cut and diagonally plaited on the sides.

Size as illustrated: 40×41 in.

Late coastal Tiahuanaco. Central or south coast of Peru. Pl. CXLVII.

352

PONCHO SHIRT OR TUNIC, incomplete, of interlocked tapestry. In its present state this shirt represents about one-half the original specimen with the seam which once ran from the arm opening to the lower edge of the shirt now placed along the center. The design is a highly conventionalized treatment of heads which cannot positively be identified as either human, animal or bird, alternating with incomplete versions of the stepped grec figure. These are separated by plain stripes, as is usual in this Tiahuanaco-derived style. (See no. 351.)

Warp: Z-spun S-doubled cotton.

Weft: Z-spun S-doubled wool.

Count: 27×116 (22×102).

Length: about 21½ in.

Width: 41 in.

Size as illustrated: 43×41 in.

Late coastal Tiahuanaco. Central or south coast of Peru. Pl. CXLVIII.

353

PONCHO SHIRT of interlocked tapestry with eccentric details. All-over patterns of eye-mouth and stepped grec motifs are similar to those of nos. 351 and 352. Perhaps unusual are the dark plain neck and arm openings.

Warp: Z-spun S-doubled cotton.

Weft: Z-spun S-doubled wool.

Count: 28×118.

Length: 24½ in.

Width: 94 in.

Heading: (1) interlocked loops.
          (2) cut and diagonally plaited.

Size as illustrated: 47×49 in.

Late coastal Tiahuanaco. Central or south coast of Peru.
Pl. CXLIX.

354 (214)

PORTION OF A PONCHO SHIRT of interlocked and eccentric tapestry. The debased or conventionalized head motif is combined with the stepped grec figure. These are arranged in opposing pairs of unequal proportions, giving pre-eminence either to the eye and mouth elements or to the stepped grec units. This is only one side of the shirt.

Warp: Z-spun, S-doubled; brown and white cotton, all wool, or cotton and wool.

Weft: Z-spun S-doubled wool.

Count: 26–29×98–114.

Length: 21 in. complete.

Width: 56 in. as folded. At least 22 in. has been folded under, so loom width originally was about 78 in.

Heading: (1) interlocked loops.
          (2) cut and diagonally plaited at the terminal end.

Size as illustrated: 56×21 in.

Late coastal Tiahuanaco. Central or south coast of Peru.
Pl. CL.

355 (230)

FRAGMENT OF INTERLOCKED TAPESTRY. This specimen is an excellent example of the distortion in design typical of many Tiahuanaco textiles. It shows an anthropomorphic bird-headed staff-bearing figure, repeated four times. The two figures at the bottom face each other and are inverted. This is truly confusing, and also the picture is complicated by the unequal proportions of the figures. The fragment came from the terminal end of the loom and apparently there had been some miscalculation in the space allotted to the design units. At the lower right, a generous amount of weft has been devoted to the wing appendages and one leg, whereas the second leg is very narrow and the staff is absent. In the right top figure the reverse is true. The other two figures at the left are even more cramped, with a wing lacking from the lower and a staff from the upper.

Warp: Z-spun S-doubled cotton.

Weft: Z-spun S-doubled wool.

Count: 42×104 (in yellow stripe) and 138 in one green area.

Length: 6½ in. Width: 13¼ in., both incomplete.

Heading: cut and plaited, then bound.

Late coastal Tiahuanaco. Central or south coast of Peru.
Pl. CLI, *left.*

356 (228)

FRAGMENT OF INTERLOCKED TAPESTRY. Two rows of blocks alternating a face consisting of two eyes and a mouth, and a purely geometric motif. Also, one row is of debased half-head, hand and stepped grec pattern. The arrangement is unusual in this style.

Warp: Z-spun S-doubled cotton.

Weft: Z-spun S-doubled wool.

Count: 32×134.

Length: 5½ in. incomplete.

Width: 15 in. incomplete.

Heading: cut and diagonally plaited.

Late coastal Tiahuanaco. South coast of Peru.
Pl. CLI, *right.*

357 (232)

MANTLE OR WALL HANGING of warp stripes with a tapestry border. This piece is of peculiar interest since it is composed of four separately woven fabrics sewn together. Many complete Peruvian fabrics are actually made of at least two joined pieces and are designed to match each other in size. In this case, however, there was a discrepancy in the sizes of the fabrics constructed, so that the warp stripe elements in the center were considerably shorter than the tapestry. This was overcome by adding, through interlocking the warp ends, about 12 inches to each of the warp stripe sections. It is observable at opposing ends of the central sections in the slightly lighter shade of brown and some irregularity in the width of the red and yellow stripes. On the central portion, simple red and yellow narrow stripes are joined with a broad brown stripe. Each stripe portion of the tapestry has five zigzag and figured rows as well as a final band of elaborate puma heads with crested headdress. The protruding tongues suggest Nazca trophy heads.

Warp and weft: Z-spun S-doubled wool in warp stripe.

Warp, and weft: Z-spun S-doubled cotton, weft wool in tapestry.

Warp, stripe portion:

> Counts: (1) 106×18, patch 72×15.
> (2) 112×18, patch 96×116.
>
> Length: originally 84 in. now 97–99 in.
>
> Width: 53½ in. (total of the two loom widths).
>
> Heading: 2 heavy cords.

Warp, tapestry portions:

> Counts: 19×118 and 22×108.
>
> Length: 13¼ in.
>
> Width of each: 101½ in. average.
>
> Heading: (1) 1 cord.
> (2) ends cut and diagonally plaited.
>
> Size as shown: 100×79 in.

Late phase of Tiahuanaco. South coast of Peru. Pl. CLII. Detail, Pl. CLIII.

358, 359, 360 (216, 217, 218)

SQUARE HATS OF PILE CLOTH. The three hats illustrated on Pl. CLIV are typical of coastal Tiahuanaco, no. 359 (*bottom*) shows a human figure with a staff. All such hats have four corners with tassels. The basic fabric is of a single-element knotted technique in which wool is looped through the knots during construction. The wool is later cut evenly to form the pile.

> Dimensions: no. 358, *center*. Height: 4¼ in. Circumference: 18¾ in.
>
> no. 359, *bottom*. Height: 4⅞ in. Circumference: 21 in.
>
> no. 360, *top*. Height: 4¼ in. Circumference: 19¼ in.

Coastal Tiahuanaco. South coast of Peru. Pl. CLIV.

361 (225)

SLIT-CENTER SLING-TYPE HEADBAND. Wrapped warp, needle work and braid. The central portion with a short slit, wrapped in red over four bundles of yarn on each side of the division, is bordered with tubular needleworked figures. These are split-headed fish which continue down the side extension of the central separation. The ends terminate in an eight-strand braid with tasselled ends. These headbands are probably ceremonial and are constructed in a manner similar to slings.

> Yarn: Z-spun S-doubled wool.
>
> Total length: 87 in.

Late Nazca? South coast of Peru. Pl. CLV, *left.*

362 (226)

HEADBAND OF BRAIDING. This consists of a slit band between which are sewn the 14 small bird figures, separately constructed. They are made in a braiding technique, which leaves pendant loops extending toward the outer edges as a fringe.

> Material: S-spun bast.
>
> Total length: 42 in. Central portion: 20 in.

Late central coast of Peru. Pl. CLV, *center right.*

363 (222)

HEADBAND OF TAPESTRY, slit and one faced. A series of crested figures have arms and legs extending out to the sides. Slight variations show in the leg patterns, but otherwise the figures are identical except for differences in colors: browns, yellows, reds, light blues on red background.

> Warp: S-spun Z-doubled cotton.
>
> Weft: Z-spun S-doubled wool, some cotton.
>
> Count: 21×146.
>
> Length: 96 in. including tassels.
>
> Width: 1½ in.

Late coast of Peru. Pl. CLV, *center left.*

364 (223)

BORDER FRAGMENT OF ECCENTRIC TAPESTRY. A leaf pattern in yellow, red and white on tan, with zigzags and red and white alternating in irregular lengths.

> Warp: Z-spun S-tripled white cotton.
>
> Weft: Z-spun S-doubled wool and some cotton.
>
> Count: 18×100.
>
> Length: 39 in.
>
> Width: 1¼ in. (incomplete).

Late north coast of Peru. Pl. CLV, *right.*

365 (233)

LARGE PORTION OF A MANTLE (?). Brocade with slit tapestry border and tapestry fringe. In a manner often found in late coastal specimens, the stylized bird motif repeats diagonally across the cloth. The slit tapestry border in wool on cotton has a central stripe of birds flying above boats, the latter an unusual subject in textiles. This in turn is bordered on both sides with continuous interlocked bird figures with a final tapestry fringe at the lower edge.

> Warp and weft: Z-spun S-doubled cotton.

Brocade yarn: Z-spun S-doubled wool, in pairs.

Count: 32×32.

Length: 27 in. (incomplete).

Width: 14½ in. complete and sewn to a fragment 4 in.

Heading: 2 cords, 2 yarns each.

Size of specimen: 27× 17½–19 in., and fringe 2⅜ in.

Late central coast of Peru. Pl. CLVI.

366

FRAGMENT OF BROCADE and transposed warp pattern. Two large long-beaked ibexes, geometrically stylized, are bordered by step-grecs. This piece is made up of six separately woven fabrics, two in brocade, and four in warp patterning. Both elements are typical of central coastal styles.

Warp: Z-spun S-doubled cotton.

Weft: Z-spun S-doubled cotton.

Count: Brocade, 48×35 average. Warp pattern, 42×30 average.

Heading: 2 cords.

Size as shown: 63×30 in.

Late central coast of Peru. Fig. 30.

367 (227)

FRAGMENT OF THE CORNER OF A SHAWL (?). Slit tapestry bordered with one faced interlocked weft pattern. The cat figures are separated by borders of scrolls arranged in steps, two at the top and four at the bottom. The final border is a step fret. This piece has been a decorated corner on a white cotton fabric, a few yarns of which can be seen along the cut edges.

Warp: Z-spun S-doubled cotton.

Weft: Z-spun S-doubled wool, cotton and Z-spun wool.

Count: 19× 82 in doubled yarns and 133 in single yarns.

Maximum dimensions: 9×9 in. (incomplete).

Late central coast of Peru. Pl. CLIX, *left.*

368

COMPLETE FABRIC OF SLIT TAPESTRY with two borders in interlocked weft pattern. Three rows of flying birds hold trophy heads in their mouths. The separation of these major bands by narrow stripes and rows of small birds gives a pleasing balanced effect. The bordering pattern is in a style which can be found from Trujillo on the north coast of Peru to Chile.

Fig. 30. *Fragment of brocaded cloth.* (Cat. No. 366.)

Warp: Z-spun S-doubled cotton.

Weft: Z-spun cotton and S-doubled wool.

Count: 21× 112.

Length: 22 in.

Width: 16¼ in.

Heading: no heading cords. Wefts start and end in warp-end loops.

Late central or south coast of Peru. Pl. CLVII.

369 (224)

FRAGMENT OF SPLIT TAPESTRY. Two large bird-demon figures have trophy heads extending downward from their beaks. The border on three sides has series of variously colored small conventionalized birds.

Warp: S-spun Z-doubled, and Z-spun and S-doubled cotton.

Weft: Z-spun S-doubled cotton and wool.

Count: 18×80 (cotton), 70 (green wool), 93 (red wool).

Length 13 in. (incomplete).

Width: 26¼ in. (24½ in. at narrower top).

Heading: 2 cords.

Late central coast of Peru. Pl. CLX, *top.*

370 (221)

LARGE EMBROIDERED MANTLE, SHAWL OR CLOAK. Embroidered in the direction of the warp, there are six rows of five figures each. They each have legs and arms outspread, elaborate headdress and enclosing ornamental patterns in the form of pendant flowering (?) branches.

Warp and weft: S-spun brown cotton in basic fabric.

Supplementary yarns: Z-spun brown cotton; yellow and red Z-spun S-doubled wool. All pairs.

Count: 27×13.

Length: 90 in.; with fringe 92½ in.

Width as shown: 67 in. This consists of three complete pieces sewn together down the sides.

Heading: One cord of 4 yarns and 5 rows of paired yarns in Z-spun cotton.

Late north coast, possibly southern portion of Chimu area near the time of Inca conquest. Pl. CLVIII. Detail, Pl. CLIX, *right.*

371

FRAGMENT OF INTERLOCKED WEFT PATTERN, one faced. There are block-strips of stylized birds, also another of interlocked snake heads with plain stripes separating them. This is an arrangement characteristic of the period. Nothing quite like this construction is made by our weavers today. The pattern wefts interlock as in tapestry, but the technique cannot be classified as tapestry.

Warp: Z-spun S-doubled cotton.

Weft: Z-spun S-doubled wool.

Count: 36×100.

Length: 5½ in. (incomplete).

Width: 5¾ in. (incomplete).

Heading: 2 rows, each of one cotton yarn.

Side: 1 side has double warp.

Inca period, central coast of Peru. Pl. CLX, *bottom.*

372 (215)

PONCHO SHIRT of interlocked and eccentric tapestry. In a typical Inca pattern-arrangement for shirts, the conventionalized human figures of late coastal styles are arranged in stepped blocks around the neck opening. On the bottom border there are two rows of a pink-on-red spatulate motif, obviously a stylization of feathers as depicted on Inca and earlier shirts.

An interesting feature of this shirt is the manner in which the neck opening was created. In this area, the warps, instead of running the full length of the loom (in this case, the width of the shirt), were probably turned about a cord running transversely across the loom. On completion of weaving, this cord was withdrawn and the freed loops interlocked.

Warp: Z-spun S-doubled wool.

Weft: Z-spun S-doubled wool.

Count: 31×116–126.

Length: 29½ in.

Width: 69½ in.

Headings: interlocked loops.

Size as illustrated: 34¾×29½ in.

Inca period, central or south coast. Pl. CLXII.

373

PONCHO SHIRT of interlocked tapestry. This is an outstanding specimen of Inca-period weaving, notable for the fine spinning, diversified decoration and colors, compact weaving and excellent preservation. In fact, it is in such unusually good condition that observations on the techniques of manufacture are difficult since all the edges are bound.

Each side of the poncho is a checkerboard divided into squares which contain no less than twenty-one units of design, not counting variations in color. These blocks are not placed rhythmically but were introduced capriciously at the whim of the weaver. The unit illustrated in fig. 31, *lower left,* evidently represents in miniature the design for a complete shirt of the type of which it is part (in other repetitions the actual neckline appears). Hence it is possible that this shirt as a whole should be regarded as a fashion plate or a conscious exhibition of technical proficiency like our eighteenth- and nineteenth-century samplers.

Fig. 31. *Units of design from the poncho-shirt* illustrated in Pl. CLXI. (Cat. No. 373.)

Some of the individual motifs are well known not on textiles but painted on pottery or on wooden drinking vessels known to the Inca as *keros*. Finally, regarding the symbolism of the individual blocks, Spanish historians report that the Inca had methods for depicting the heavens and it is possible that some at least of these decorations represent constellations or groups of stars.

Warp: Z-spun S-doubled cotton.

Weft: Z-spun S-doubled wool.

Count: 48×273.

Length: 30¼ in.

Width: 72 in. The loom length is the entire width of the shirt.

Sides: Reinforced with 5 multiple warps.

Heading: All of interlocked loops.

Inca period, Ica style. South coast of Peru. Pl. CLXI, and fig. 31.

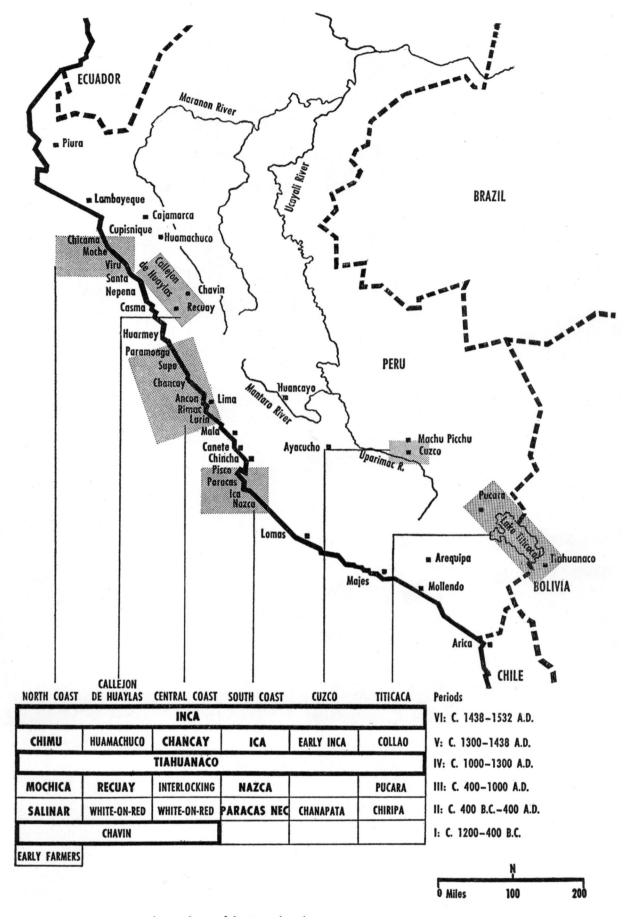

NORTH COAST	CALLEJON DE HUAYLAS	CENTRAL COAST	SOUTH COAST	CUZCO	TITICACA	Periods
INCA						VI: C. 1438–1532 A.D.
CHIMU	HUAMACHUCO	CHANCAY	ICA	EARLY INCA	COLLAO	V: C. 1300–1438 A.D.
TIAHUANACO						IV: C. 1000–1300 A.D.
MOCHICA	RECUAY	INTERLOCKING	NAZCA		PUCARA	III: C. 400–1000 A.D.
SALINAR	WHITE-ON-RED	WHITE-ON-RED	PARACAS NEC	CHANAPATA	CHIRIPA	II: C. 400 B.C.–400 A.D.
CHAVIN						I: C. 1200–400 B.C.
EARLY FARMERS						

Ancient Indian Cultures of the Central Andes: REGIONAL AND TIME DIVISIONS.
After Bennett, 1954. Courtesy Museum of Modern Art, New York.

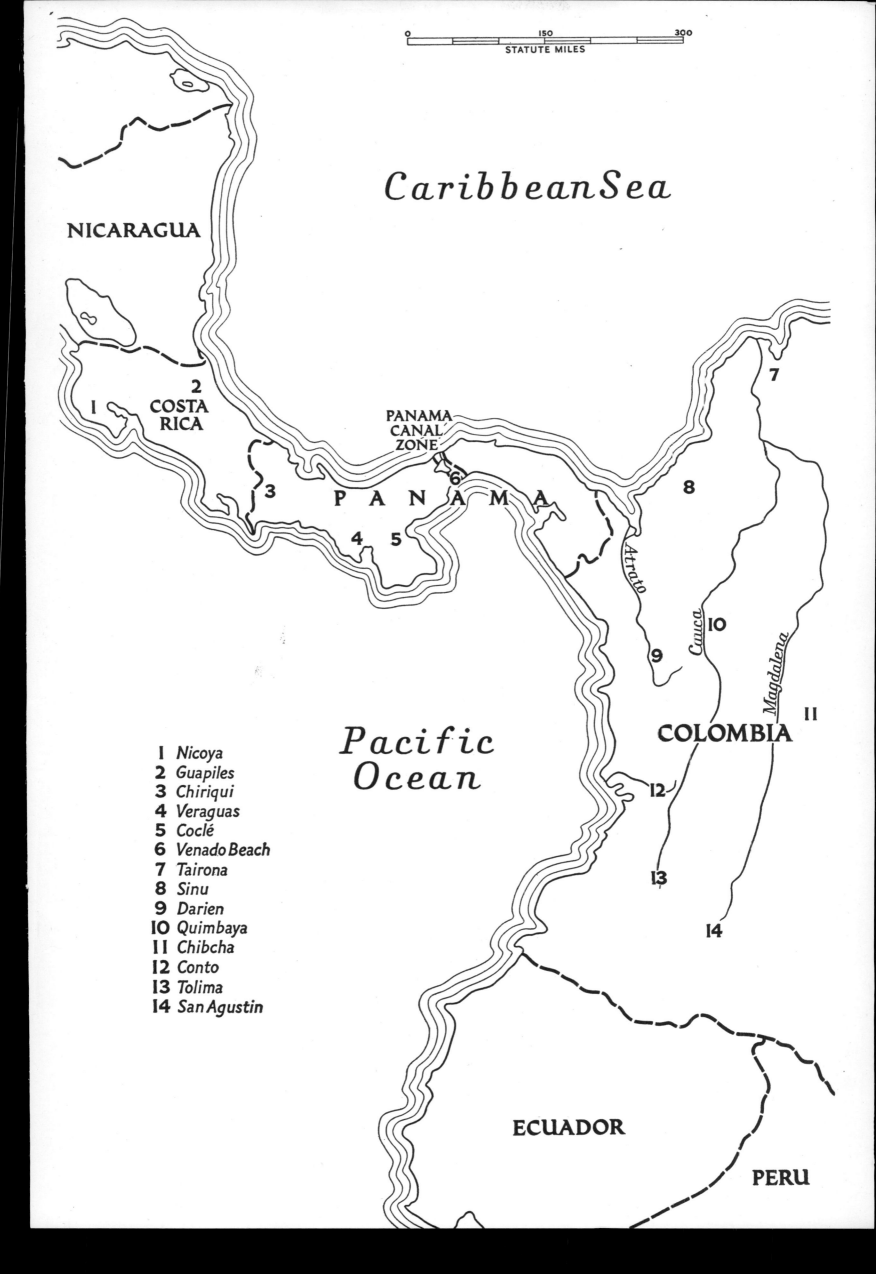

STATUTE MILES

CaribbeanSea

NICARAGUA

COSTA
RICA

PANAMA
CANAL
ZONE

PANAMA

Pacific
Ocean

Atrato

Cauca

Magdalena

COLOMBIA

1 Nicoya
2 Guapiles
3 Chiriqui
4 Veraguas
5 Coclé
6 Venado Beach
7 Tairona
8 Sinu
9 Darien
10 Quimbaya
11 Chibcha
12 Conto
13 Tolima
14 San Agustin

ECUADOR

PERU

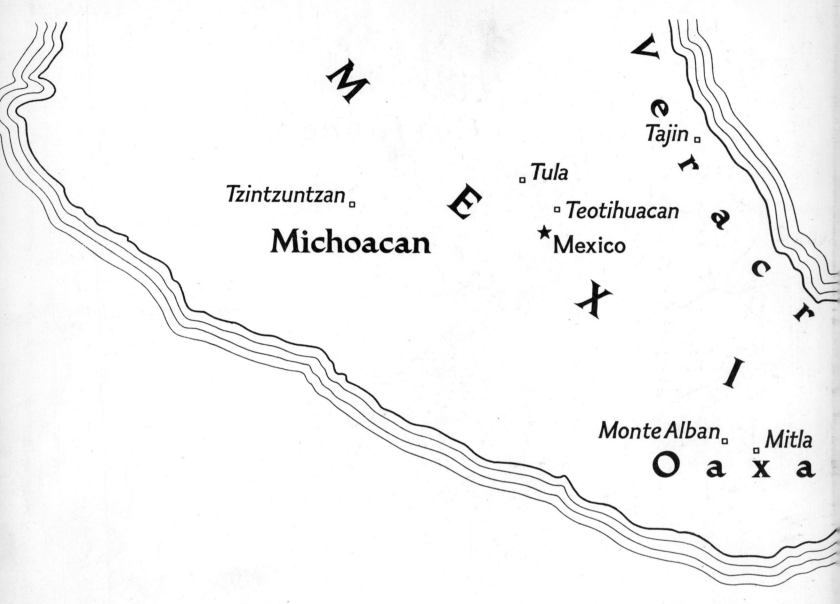

STYLE SEQUENCES AND APPROXIMATE DATES

PERIOD → / AREA ↓	PROTO-HISTORIC	POST-CLASSIC	CLASSIC	FORMATIVE (ARCHAIC) ———————
CENTRAL MEXICO	Aztec	Tula Toltec	Teotihuacan → IV III II I	Ticoman / Tlatilco / Zacatenco / Arbolillo ——
NORTH VERACRUZ	Totonac	? Classic Veracruz		
SOUTH VERACRUZ	Olmec (historic)	?	Olmec (archaeological) ———————→ / Cerro de las Mesas / Tres Zapotes ———→	
MONTE ALBAN	V (Mixtec)	IV (←———— Zapotec ————→)	III B	III A II I
LOWLAND MAYA	Proto-historic	Post-Classic	Classic Tzakol Tepeu	Pre-Classic ——————————→ Chicanel → Mamom
DATES	A.D. 1500	A.D. 1100	A.D. 700	A.D. 300 100 B.C. 500 B.C. 900 B.C.